VIKING SUMMER

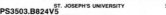
VIKING
SUMMER

BY
CHARLES A. BRADY

THE BRUCE PUBLISHING COMPANY
MILWAUKEE

For the Four Originals, Especially
KRISTIN MORE

Rosary College Dewey Classification Number: 813

Library of Congress Catalog Card Number: 56–13194

© 1956 BY THE BRUCE PUBLISHING COMPANY
MADE IN THE UNITED STATES OF AMERICA

Contents

VIKING SUMMER

CHAPTER ONE

Retreat from Summer

LIKE all retreats, the Desmond family's retreat from summer had been sad, slow, reluctant. First, the long, low little cottage on the Canadian shore, so eggshell white of stucco, so Mediterranean coral of trim, had to be closed and shuttered against the Ontario winter. The canoe had to be stored in the garage — Professor Desmond, who hunted sometimes in the fall, set up his decoy ducks in the thwarts. The chrysanthemums were pinched back and hooded; the water turned off; the outdoor grill lodged in the bathhouse; the picnic table, on the screened porch, turned up against the wall to protect its varnished top; the sand toys stacked in sharp-edged metal rows; the fireplace swept and garnished. The car was loaded to the gunwales with the impedimenta that always waited till the last trip: radio; typewriter; red Mackinaw; two wooden Swedish ladies from Dalecarlia who, in the summer months, had their skirts plumped out into two bouffant bells with party napkins.

The Siamese cats, Rajah and Ranee, and the venerable black short-hair, Mr. Sillerton Jackson, took it hard, too. Rajah's pansy face creased in an ostentatious yawn, Ranee opened her blue eyes the wider, somnolent Sillerton let his pink tongue loll out, while the four children filed by them, arms piled high with books and sweaters and bathing suits. Circassian slaves, that's what we are, said Professor Desmond to himself, fair-skinned Circassian slaves for these tawny-coated royalties. And sometimes they looked more arrogantly Eastern than others. In the middle of the night, for example, when Kristin

1

stirred in her sleep and Professor Desmond went nervously up the
stairs to see if all was well, Rajah and Ranee, who slept on the living-
room couch, would watch him, aloof, mysterious, the white ruffs surrounding their dark triangular faces snowier than ever in the half-light
of four a.m., the Nilotic profiles more Pharaoh-like even than in daylight, the sheathed claws tucked under Sphinx-straight chests.

It was also necessary to bid adieu to the lake and shore. The
September air seemed clearer and the pebbles at the water's edge
more sharply defined and separate now than in summer. Smoke
went up from an occasional chimney — thin and blue. The New
York shore was more distinct than usual. Not a leaf had dropped yet
from the huge poplar whose silver roots lay exposed from the
erosion of the shore line — things bloomed later and dropped later
in this cool Canadian air. The tap roots went very deep, but the
great old tree was becoming dangerous. It should be felled. Professor
Desmond made a mental note to speak to Norman Larned about it.

Out over the blue lake a gull swooped and struck a fish. The small
perch glinted silver in the strong yellow beak. Professor Desmond
thought of sea kings and their Northmen's quarry. There was really
something Viking in this northern landscape, in the cool wash of
air flooding down from Labrador. This blue-eyed lake of Erie could,
without warning, lash itself into berserker fury. In winter it wore
frost rime in its beard. Or was this too much of a pathetic fallacy
even for a teacher of English in a small western New York college
near Buffalo? He smiled. Etymologically speaking, too, it was a
fallacy. Erie was the Cat Lake, the Lake of the Eries, of the people
of the Cat Nation. It was an Indian panther lake, cat-pawed, wind-
flawed, quick-pouncing. It had puma-candid eyes, as blue as the
murderously innocent blue of Rajah's and Ranee's. Or was this going
too far in another direction now? Professor Desmond smiled again
and lit a cigarette from his *Players* pack.

No, he said to himself, no, it was a metaphysical impossibility to
overdo things when it came to expressing nature. But, even though
the redmen had been here first, Viking caught the northern inscape
of this land. There was even a reputed Viking sword find in this
region. They had it now in a Toronto museum. The scholars were
still very much at loggerheads over the authenticity of the sword.

But it began to appear much better than an outside possibility that the sword was genuine.

Stifling a yawn, Professor Desmond came to himself with a start. He had better stop woolgathering and get on with this tedious business of removal from lakeshore to town. After three fugitive months of Canadian moons and Erie sunsets, it was high time to evacuate this beach head, which his meager professor's salary, supplemented by his mother's original gift, had so hardly wrested from the unknown terrain of quitclaim and mortgage. Time to invest the city once again. But there was one more immemorial rite still to discharge — their final shopping splurge in Ridgeway. He stubbed out the cigarette against a boulder.

Mrs. Desmond stayed behind, setting the kitchen to rights for the thousandth time, while the four girls and their father drove down the Queen's Highway to Ridgeway. Ridgeway stood on a spine of land where, during the War of 1812, Redcoats and American Federal troops had locked in bloody battle. Today's Ridgeway was a pleasant English-style village whose main street was lined with neatly-kept wool and china shops, and with two drugstores, which had only lately left off calling themselves apothecaries' shops.

"Look, Dad," Kristin said, pointing to one of the showcases in the wool and china shop. "Look. A mouse in a blouse."

It was more than just any mouse in any blouse. It was a dainty china mouse in dimity and mobcap. In point of fact, it was the Lady Mouse from The Tailor of Gloucester. And she happened to have been considerably knocked down in price in an end-of-season sale, alongside such other notable residents of Nurseryland as Samuel Whiskers and Tom Kitten. Professor Desmond thought the Lady Mouse would look perfect, back in the city house, in the fireside alcove above their china Walrus and Carpenter and Tweedledum and Tweedledee.

"How much is the Lady Mouse?" he asked the shopgirl who was moving bolts of plaid-bright woolen goods from one shelf to another.

"Which mouse?" asked the shopgirl to whom the Lady Mouse, the Town Mouse, and the Country Mouse were all one: just so many pieces of china bric-a-brac for the American tourist trade.

"The mouse in the blouse," Kristin said again with four-year-old doggedness.

The shopgirl held up one of the figurines.

"No," said Professor Desmond politely. "That is Pigling Bland — a pig. The one we want is the Lady Mouse from *The Tailor of Gloucester*."

He tapped on the showcase just above where the Lady Mouse was holding up her tiny china mirror in Keatsian repose, a still unravished mouse bride of quietness.

"This one," he said.

And, as the shopgirl hesitated:

"She will be marked on her bottom."

Moira, ten, and Sheila, eight, giggled. Karen, fourteen, blushed. The shopgirl looked as if she suspected liberties were being taken by the tanned American gentleman with the four daughters. Professor Desmond felt a shy man's anger at his own inadvertency.

"Yes," said Kristin, who had been following the shopgirl's hovering hand. "That's the one — the mouse in the blouse."

The shopgirl wrapped up Karen's Chanel, a swan-necked Wedgwood gravy boat circled by a frieze of Griffins against a blue ground for Mother, the Lady Mouse and two Dickens figurines — Pecksniff and the Artful Dodger — for Father. For the third straight year Professor Desmond covetously hefted a Royal Doulton Falstaff in plum-colored velvet slops and gilded doublet; and as reluctantly abandoned it. It seemed as if, year by year, he had less and less money for primroses, for the simple and sufficient reason that he had to spend so much more money for bread.

A fine rain was beginning to fall when the five of them came out of the trim little shop with the old-fashioned bow window — there was just enough rain to cause the windshield wipers to swish as they drove back to Crescent Beach to pick up Mother. A cold mist was blowing in from the lake as the Desmond Chevrolet, listing a little from the unaccustomed load, lurched over the tracks that ran parallel to the Queen's Highway on the last lap to the Peace Bridge; and, once that border barrier was crossed, to autumn, school, and home. The Siamese, who were inveterate motorists, settled down at once atop the back seat luggage, but old Sillerton Jackson set up his special I-don't-like-autos wail. The mournful sound seemed to make their retreat from summer all the more final.

On the American side of the Peace Bridge Professor Desmond bought a late edition *News*. There was a photograph of a hooded man on the front page.

"Who's the feller in the Ku Klux outfit, Toby?" he asked Mother, turning right on Niagara Street.

For some reason, Mother's voice sounded a little troubled.

"It's the Russian code clerk who defected from the Ottawa legation," she said. "He's living in Ontario now, John; and he wears the hood so his face can't be photographed."

"Ontario?" said Professor Desmond, interested. "What part of Ontario?"

"It doesn't say," she said. "It's supposed to be a secret."

"A rather melodramatic precaution, I should say," said Professor Desmond, beginning to whistle *Valentina*. "Oh, well. Ontario's a big place."

Mrs. Desmond looked across the rain-misted river at Ontario, and shivered a little. If Ontario was big, it was also close. And the way things were going in the world, she didn't think Ontario was so very big, either. Distances were shrinking as men's hearts grew harder. She put a protective hand on Kristin's head.

Home had its compensations, however. And autumn. For the whole family there was brother Jack's furlough from Korea beginning the last week in October. For Mother there were her roses still blooming gloriously in the side beds near the blue spruce tree; there were the salvia flowers firing their crimson salvos against the dark green of the Japanese dwarf yews in the front plot; and everywhere the clean astringency of asters and chrysanthemums. For Father there were his books. Not that the beach house wasn't bulging with books. But the best of beach houses, whatever their other attributes, were hardly paradises for books. No bookman worth his salt willingly entrusted his treasures to damp lakeside air and silver fish.

The town house literally overflowed with books. The best way, perhaps, to sum up a family like the Desmonds was to say that theirs was a house where books were everywhere. In a colonial breakfront in the living room; in alcoves either side the formal fireplace; on the grand piano. Between blue mandarin book ends, red teak water buffalo book ends, gilt China-boy book ends. On the stair landing, in the study, in the water-tight cellar — three cases full, no less — in the kitchen, in the bedrooms, in the bathroom. It was a house overrun by sheet music, records, water colors, camel-hair brushes, puzzles, and toys as well. Oh, yes, and masquerade costumes — costumes for impromptu plays, for Halloween parties, for charades.

Yes, home had its compensations. Karen returned to her multitudinous teen-age concerns; Sheila and Moira to their own circle of pig-tailed intimates. All three girls came back to the family red-leather Kiplings with the gold elephant and mandala stamped thereon; to the bound volumes of *St. Nicholas* stretching from 1890 to 1925; to the Christmas *Chatterboxes* that ended with 1929; and to the portfolios of Rackham illustrations which Mother had collected years back before she and Father married.

Kristin's homecoming consolations were as yet, naturally enough, somewhat less literary. The child was a born pragmatist, with a controlled and most convenient sense of fantasy very much like that of Carroll's Alice. Like Alice, if she found herself suddenly falling down a rabbit hole, she would be quite capable of abstracting a jar marked JAM en route. Her framework of reference, even for a girl child, was breathtakingly egocentric. When, against orders, she waded past the sandbar that marked her outer freedom of motion, the water did not grow deeper, she "became smaller." When Rajah and Ranee, hunting in tandem — Sillerton Jackson was too old for the chase now — bagged a bird or a bunny, Professor Desmond, who had never really reconciled himself to the animal kingdom's rule of fang and claw, used to sweat and Mother used to feel sick. Not so Kristin. "I will pray for the bird," she would announce regally.

Chief among Kristin's consolations was the clown doll, Bozo. Kristin might almost be said to have created Bozo. Theologically speaking, she had certainly endowed him with both personality and soul. Like some vegetation god from Frazer, Bozo periodically underwent ritual immolation. To be more exact, Kristin had a habit of loving him one-dimensionally flat. Then, like a phoenix, he would rise again after Father paid a visit to *The Doll Hospital* where Bozos were stocked by the gross. Bozo even had a series of names. Beginning as plain Bozo, progressing through Bozo Belinda, he had lately ended up as Bozo B. Applesound Carstreet Klopp. At least, that was the way Professor Desmond phoneticized the extra names to himself. He supposed that, in etymological terms, Klopp derived from the television professor who preceded *Children's Theater* on Channel Four, that B. was an abbreviated form of the aboriginal Belinda, and that Carstreet must be — a fine commentary, incidentally, on his own professional mores — a corruption of Carstairs. Applesound he just gave up. It fitted, but its exact provenance seemed untraceable.

Professor Desmond set down his razor, the third morning after their return to the city, and stared at the squatty little blonde thing that was his fourth-born daughter. September mornings in Buffalo could be quite cold, and she was wearing the quilted bathrobe he always called her Tolstoi dressing gown. One of the few things that really irritated Mother was his half-serious insistence that the child looked like Tolstoi.

It appeared, from the dialogue going on at his feet, that Bozo had been or else was going — it was not clear which — to Westminster Abbey where, it additionally appeared, Elizabeth II had kissed him and given him both a toothbrush and a squirt gun.

While he applied an astringent, Kristin tuned in to the television band which, five mornings a week, featured those cartoon creations of the Twenties, Koko the Clown, Felix the Cat, and some of the naïver ink doodles of the pre-Disney age.

The television commercial abruptly turned into a fantasia of soap flakes dancing to the tune of Strauss' *Tales from the Vienna Woods*. Gravely Kristin led the limp-legged Bozo into the mazes of a Viennese waltz. A few tantalizing bars, and the announcer's mellifluous impersonality again cut across the formal dance.

"Tell me, Dad," said Kristin suddenly. "What does 'married' mean? Dancing?"

Professor Desmond, who taught Chaucer's *Troilus and Criseyde* and Eliot's *Four Quartets*, was struck by the child's answer to her own question. Yes, it was a dance all right. The oldest dance in the world. And trust a girl child, however young, to sniff out a wedding cake, however distant. There was a wedding in the offing, so soon as brother Jack got back from Korea. But, officially, no one — not even Karen — was supposed to know. Apparently female pores drank in wedding intimations by osmosis.

"Yes, Kristin," he said gently, rumpling her hair. "It means dancing. Among other things."

Frying bacon was sending its morning incense through the house, as the two of them came downstairs. It was washday. Mother, married twenty-two years this August past, was not in the habit of dancing much on Mondays. Nor was Professor Desmond, who had to make a third-hour class in the *Age of Johnson*. But Kristin and Bozo danced every day. As he turned the car out of the blacktopped drive, he saw the two red heads bobbing up and down across the sun-shot green of the September lawn. Counting Bozo, there were four red heads and one blonde among the children: Sheila Titian red, Kristin gold red, Karen russet fall-leaf red, Bozo Ringling Brothers poster-red, and Moira flaxen as Rapunzel in the tower.

CHAPTER TWO

Reprieve from Winter

OCTOBER had been stormy. High winds, blowing off the lake, and stinging rains had lashed the little beach house, weathering the shutters further, making damp spots on the stucco. The day before Halloween, a calm fell over the autumn lake; the rain-washed air became clear and cold. The great northern presences began to close in about the little house. But there would be still one more reprieve from winter.

Professor Desmond set down his coffee spoon.

"Another coffee, Toby, please," he called to his wife.

She did not answer at once. She and Karen were having one of their interminable recent conferences. It puzzled Professor Desmond, who like most men rarely looked back, how women found so much to talk about in the endless trivia of their personal pasts. They seemed to be gifted — or should one rather say, cursed? — with an uncanny power of total and, even more astounding, chronological recall. It was as if they dragged behind them an ever lengthening chain of reminiscence — one they ecstatically fettered on themselves like the penitential links of the old desert Fathers. One would not think offhand that a child of fourteen years would have so much to remember.

Professor Desmond listened and, at once, found himself chastened for his bright male cynicism of the moment before.

"Of course, I don't trust everybody," Karen was saying in refutation of some point or other Mother had quite obviously just made. "In fact, the only person I've ever completely trusted is Dad."

9

Wow! said Professor Desmond to himself, touched out of all proportion. That tears it. Trust like this, the unearned increment of fatherhood, surely should be accepted in a spirit of grateful humility. Thursday was his one day free from classes, but he decided to help Mother prune and mulch the roses instead of, as he had voluptuously intended a minute previous, cutting the pages of the new Mauriac.

He was just replacing trellis number one when Sheila and Moira, all dressed up for their school Halloween party, rode by on their bicycles on the return trip after lunch. Moira's costume offered no particular difficulty in the way of identification. Moira was an Indian again. Sheila's identity, however, was another thing altogether. A sort of veil, whose exact significance momentarily eluded him, floated out in the breeze from under a sort of tropical topee.

Professor Desmond, garden shears in hand, made the two a formal bow.

"Dr. Livingstone, I presume," he said to Sheila.

"Oh, Daddy," said Sheila. "I'm a nun."

"Sister Mary Joseph Flight from Egypt, I presume, then?" he asked. "Or is it Sister Mary Paschal Candle Lit? Or, possibly, Sister Mary of the Sacred Heart Exposed?"

"You got that from Karen," the Indian pointed out.

"So I did, so I did," said Professor Desmond, unabashed. "But I haven't used it in some time. Besides, plagiarism is a professorial privilege." Then he added:

"Why the veil?"

"I'm a postulant," said Sheila.

"Ah," said Professor Desmond, making a mental note that a new twist in Halloween costumes would be for a whole convent to parade as penguins. It wouldn't be expensive, either. They already had their penguin suits. And any old false-face nose would do.

The children pedalled off again. Mother, muffled in a turtleneck sweater, came out of the garage, dragging a tub of peat moss behind her.

"We'll start with the Maréchal Niels," she said matter-of-factly.

While Professor Desmond mulched the Maréchal Niels, Mother tidied up the adjoining bed that still flushed pink, even on this last day of October.

Over by a mound of leaves marked down for evening burning so soon as dusk should fall, Kristin and her friend, Suzanne Jensen, were at their everlasting bride game. Both knelt in the red leaves in nuptial expectation.

"The trouble with that game," said Professor Desmond, lighting a cigarette, "is that there are too many brides and no bridegrooms. Our little friends seem to have reversed the old saying to read: *Always a bride, never a bridesmaid.*"

"Suzanne is groom today," said Mother, snipping off a dead root. "I heard them arranging it through the kitchen window."

Just then Suzanne burst narcissistically into her favorite song.

"O Susanna," she sang, "don't you cry for me!"

Kristin was affronted. "Stop it, Suzanne!" she said indignantly. "Grooms don't sing in church!"

"I did," said Professor Desmond. "I sang *Auprès de ma blonde* all during Mass. To myself, of course. But I guess grooms' mothers don't do much singing."

He touched Mother on her hair which was as brown as brown could be, not blonde at all.

"About Jack, Toby," he said awkwardly. "It's not too soon. War matures a boy. Ellen's a nice girl. We'll get along."

Then, as she still stayed pensive:

"*La condition humaine*, you know," he said, "And the best part of the human predicament, from any point of view. It renews one's sense of poetry."

Still she did not stir.

"*Sweet Thames, run softly,*" he urged her. "You used to like Patmore, Toby. Remember?"

And he quoted in the smoke-blue afternoon:

"*Love wakes men, once a lifetime each;*
They lift their heavy lids, and look;
And lo, what one sweet page can teach
They read with joy, then shut the book.
And some give thanks, and some blaspheme,
And most forget; but, either way,
That and the Child's unheeded dream
Is all the light of all their day."

Kristin and Suzanne were no longer bride and groom. Shrieking like little banshees, they ran in and out of the mound of leaves, scuffing the leaves into gold and crimson flight. A brace of starlings flew up as the children romped. Kristin stopped short suddenly.

"Leaves and birds, leaves and birds," she said to Suzanne. "The leaves don't think they're leaves, they think they're birds. And the birds don't think they're birds, they think they're leaves."

The sun was sinking fast. A breath of decay wafted up from the damp earth where the children's racing feet had laid bare the wet black soil. Another hour and they could light the jack-o'-lanterns in the dining-room windows. Professor Desmond thought he might anticipate the leaf burning a little. Striking a match, he touched it to the brittle, fragrant pile. A little tongue of flame ran through the mound. Mother took her bamboo rake and evened the frayed edges of the pile. The flame caught fast. First one heard a hissing, then a crackling. A pungent incense began to fill the blue-hazed yard.

There was something really atavistic about the tamed anarchy of bonfires, especially when one reached the great divide of the year, when weather poised, as now, on the windy ridgepole of the world, and October's gold made ready to give way to the silver of November. Professor Desmond's Ulster ancestors had called this night the Feast of Samhain, the Night of the Dead. It was still the Night of the Dead in New World's folkways: ten cent store high jinks in a graveyard; ghosts walking in papier-mâché; white skeletons sewed in black cloth outside the flesh instead of in. He couldn't see that altering the name to Halloween, the Feast of All Hallows, had made much difference. The desperate revelry, the whistling past a cemetery, was still pagan in essence.

Or maybe it had made some little difference. A rising wind scattered some of the smoking leaves that were beginning to be ghost-ash now. Wind shadows coursed the yard. It was as if great presences, archangelic-tall, wielding some breeze-brash rake, some broom of air, were tidying these gardens against the time of frost. The kindly annealing flame made mortality smell fragrant. Not just in his yard, either. Other bonfires in other yards smoked into the watchful early darkness; in the MacDonalds' yard, in the Starks'. A feeling of great friendliness, of communion with humankind, took possession of his heart. It was as if a sense of camaraderie warmed itself into life at all the bonfires along the leaf-deep street. It was a sacramental thing, this burning of leaves, this cleansing, this baptism by fire.

Leaning on the rake, Professor Desmond wondered how it was with the little summer cottage in this leaf-loud October dark. When one loved, there was empathy as well as sympathy. But, of course, the beach house wasn't really shut up today at all. Jack, one week back from Korea, and four days short of his wedding, was there with Ellen, getting things ready for tonight's Halloween party. It was to be a good old-fashioned Desmond masquerade — with a few new wrinkles thrown in, contrived by Jack's and Ellen's friends from one of the Buffalo radio stations. The ghosties and ghoulies and long leggity beasties and things that went bump in the dark were going to get a spot of assistance from the newest electronic devices dreamed up by man the wizard.

The older Desmonds weren't going — nor the young ones, either. Karen was, though — her first really grown-up party.

Rajah and Ranee skittered through the leaves. Now there, said Professor Desmond to himself, were two characters who didn't have to put on fancy dress. Life was a perpetual masquerade for them. Who were they, really, underneath those singed marshmallow pelts? They were out of Perrault, certainly, not from Grimm. Their movements were like smoke out of some Arabian Wadi. When they boxed, the air seemed full of flying empress bumble bees. They were miniature genii with chocolate paws and pansy faces and almond ruffs. They were furred goblins, peripatetic Buddhas, orchid lovely creatures strayed from some Chinese scroll.

A little hand clutched Professor Desmond's trouser leg.

"Boo!" said Kristin from behind her sheet.

"Boo!" said Suzanne.

"Boo!" said Bozo in Kristin's voice. Bozo, too, was habited in a tiny sheet. His hair was disconcertingly red against the dead white of his cerement.

At the Desmonds' cottage on the Canadian Shore, Karen, dressed as Puck, red hair against leaf green of summer sunsuit, sat, withdrawn a little, beside the beach house fireplace where drift wood bluely burned again; and watching those Olympian masquers dance who were separated from her in time by so few years but by light years in experience. Yet, in certain ways, Karen was older than they would ever be. Although she was as leggy still as Horace's fawn, the classic curves of womanhood began to catch the eye. She had never passed through the fleeting and distracting phase the French call *beauté du diable*; and never would. It was better so. That bouquet evanesced almost at once. Like some other wines of experience, it did not travel well. It was a flower without roots. Here were good roots. When the flower suddenly broke from the tightly folded bud, the splendor would be the greater for the slow maturing.

So far the party had gone off perfectly. There was no moon riding the heavens, but the bright Canadian stars pulsed prodigally in the clear night. It was still and cold. Every now and then one of the few remaining walnuts snapped in the frost, bouncing with a hollow pong off the green Chevrolet hood beneath the tree from which they fell. A brown cowled monk, wearing a skeleton mask and swinging a red lantern, had met the party as the cars turned into the asphalt parking area behind the cottage. Jim Harrison, who worked in a radio station, was made up as Dracula, crimson-lined opera cloak and all. On a sawhorse coffin, two candles burning at either end, reclined a most convincing corpse. There was a gorilla and a Frankenstein monster with green luminous paint on its face. Several thugs, *species Americana*. Another thug, Indian variety. His fellow, a murdering dacoit in white turban and red sash. And, naturally, a capering red devil complete with pitchfork and tail.

The girls were less painstakingly macabre. Ellen had come as an artist in floppy velvet tam-o'-shanter, smock, and velvet trousers, a jeweled scatter pin in the shape of a tiny palette on one shoulder. A clinging ground mist, which had lifted only an hour ago, had seemed to bruise the glossy velvet and to fix the gardenia scent Ellen always used, until it became more hauntingly pervasive even than usual. The girl's face in the firelight, as she danced by with Jack, was that of a great dreaming gardenia opening under the moon — a girl gardenia with eyes of cornflower blue. Karen had never seen Ellen look so lovely — nor Jack, who was a Pierrot, so tenderly attentive. She propped her chin, and watched. Here was a mystery flowering, petal by perfumed petal, before her eyes.

Jack was a brother and a champion athlete and a soldier and a gentleman and a hero and her best friend. He was what her crowd had fallen into the habit of calling a "good Joe." He used to take her to shows, buy her *Fanny Farmer's*, and pull her red pigtails. He was the only person in the world licensed to call her "Katie." Now he was become a lover and a god as well. It was suddenly and breathtakingly borne in on Karen that men and women, in the brief time of their strong youth, were also gods and goddesses of the morning.

Karen had been introduced to all of the other girls, but, except for Ellen, she remembered no more than their first names. There was a Columbine, three Spanish ladies in almost identical shawls and mantillas, an Indian, a Colonial dame, and a bell boy.

The gags had all come off without a hitch. Jim Harrison had set up a portable microphone in the bath house. At set intervals, and without being detected, he cut into the dance music with the alarming announcement that a homicidal lunatic, escaped from the Buffalo State Hospital, had been last seen crossing the Peace Bridge. The mythical fugitive was reported armed with a butcher knife and a black jack. All residents of the Fort Erie, Waverly Beach, Crescent Beach, and Bertie Bay regions were warned to keep their doors locked until further notice. Owners of summer residences, now closed for the winter, were asked to surrender their keys to the Provincial Police, so that a cottage to cottage search might be made. It created a delicious panic among the girls and a pleasurable uneasiness among those boys who were not in on the know.

Between announcements Jim Harrison stepped from the bath house into the kitchen for a quick one. There was rye, Scotch, sherry; and, for Karen, Coca Cola. She found Jim in the kitchen, popping peanuts into his long Egyptian face. Give Jim Harrison a stylized chin beard, and he would be a Hyksos Pharaoh in a sack suit. He liked Karen.

"Hi, kid," he said, tossing her a bag of peanuts, and knocking off a Cola cap. "Drink up. O.K.?"

"O.K.," said Karen after a long draw on her straw. "When does the big witching begin?"

The "big witching" was designed to be the evening's premier

turn. At precisely midnight Harrison would cut in on the radio again with a prepared spiel about the ghost of the old French buccaneer who was said to haunt the Canadian shore between Point Abino — Abineau originally — and the old Fort at Fort Erie. According to the legend, which Harrison had invented out of whole cloth, each Halloween the pirate, L'Ollonais, rowed ashore somewhere along the coast and there re-enacted the murder of his boatswain and the burial of his treasure. After the masquers had had five minutes to digest this latest fiction, the fun was scheduled to begin in earnest out on the beach. Karen didn't know all the refinements of the plan. But she knew that Bud Wechsel, who was currently the death's head monk, and Ed Tremblay, currently the devil, had cooked up something special. She also knew they had a change of costume cached away in the garage, and that, a half hour earlier, they had quietly withdrawn in the direction of the garage.

Jim Harrison looked at his wrist watch.

"Time to start the caper, kid," he said, getting to his feet. "Why don't you move out on the wall and get a good seat?"

Very quietly, Karen slipped the catch on the back screened porch, and went down the paved walk in the starlight to the beach wall. Though the moon had set, the quiet lake was luminous under the night sky; it harbored in its glassy, lightly breathing mirror an infinity of drowned stars. Settling a blanket over her legs — a Puck's costume was hardly made for a Canadian All Hallows — she snuggled into an angle of the wall. Then she sat bolt upright. One of the masquers was steadily watching her from beside Browns' higher wall which made a right angle with their own. It was no one she had seen inside — of that she was sure. And it could hardly be either Bud or Ed in different costumes. They were going to be pirates, not Vikings. Besides, they were both fairly short. This man was tall.

"Hello," she said uncertainly.

The masquer did not answer. Nor did he give over his steady scrutiny of her. He was dressed as a Viking — an admirable costume, too, authentic in every detail — and leaning on an empty swordsheath, its point sunk in the sand. There was enough star radiance for Karen to be able to make out the rune waves on the sheath. He was tall, very tall; six-feet three, at the very least. And very broad of shoulder. She had seen Klondike Eric, the professional wrestler, once, sitting outside the beach grocery store in his low-slung Jaguar sports car. This man equaled him in shoulder span and surpassed him in height. The beautifully forged chain mail, molding his chest, went in and out as he breathed; each separate link gleamed silver in the starshine. He wore no mask — another point of difference from the other members of the party. But the helmet came down low on his forehead, and a golden beard could be a most effective disguise in a clean-shaven century. As Karen stared at him, he turned his head away from her and looked out on the lake.

A shiver went over her. It was as if some elder god from the far-off prime sat there in the starlight. It was only a man, of course. She knew that. Or else a very large boy masquerading as a man. Where did boy leave off and man begin, anyway? She realized, all of a sudden and for the first time, that there could be an element of primitive terror in the very fact of the male presence.

"Hello," Karen said again.

Again the Viking did not answer.

Karen was really growing a little frightened now. She did not know who the Viking could be. For one thing, she didn't remember anyone so tall among her brother's friends. For another, though she was in on the Harrison hoax about the escaped maniac, for a moment she had the panicky thought that the story was true, that Jim had taken it off the evening news tape at the studio, that a real lunatic had broken into a real costumier's and stolen this marvelous disguise.

"If you don't answer me at once," she said to the Viking, "I'll call the other masqueraders."

Just then a rocket went up from behind the old pier that was greenly rotting away three quarters of a mile or so offshore. The Pierce-Arrow people, who used to live at the other end of Crescent Beach, had, in the palmy days before World War I, once moored a yacht there. Then, in rapid succession, two more flares, accompanied by aerial bombs, went up. When Karen, shocked for a moment by the burst of light and noise, looked back toward the Viking, he was gone, with nothing more to indicate that he had been there than what appeared to be a clean cleft in the sand left by his sword sheath.

Harrison's charade had begun. The masquers came flooding out onto veranda and wall. It was one of Jim's better efforts, and Bud Wechsel and Ed Tremblay, who were buccaneer and boatswain respectively, played their uncanny roles right up to the hilt. They rowed ashore in a little dinghy from the lee of the old pier, Wechsel trolling out, in his best Chantecleer's bass, a pirate chantey, Tremblay quavering a falsetto "Ahoy!" at intervals. The costumes were effective in the calcium flare the two of them lit once they disembarked. The props were most convincing, as was the mimic fight to the death, and the hanging of the boatswain — a dummy secreted behind a screen of rocks — from the gibbet which had been improvised out of the Thibauts' swing. When L'Ollonais-Wechsel, still roaring his Yo-ho-ho!, rowed away alone into the night, the audience broke out into half-scared applause. Spirits had been invoked, hackles raised, the earth had stirred, the old gods were propitiated, and the day of All Hallows was whitely dawning. But where, said Karen to herself, had the Viking gone?

On the way home, sitting beside Jim Harrison in the front seat, and politely averting her eyes from the two murmuring couples in the back seat, Karen thought she would ask some questions. As it happened, she asked only one.

"Who was the Viking, Jim?" she asked.

Jim Harrison, whose steady girl had the flu — which was why Jim was alone — stifled a yawn.

"What Viking, kid?" he said. "There was no Viking in the caper — only pirates."

Upstairs in the dark bedroom she shared with her youngest sister, Karen smiled at the little ghost-suit neatly spread across the sleeping Bozo. Kristin turned drowsily about in her bed.

"Is the Knave of Hearts a ghost, Karen?" she asked in a small voice furred with sleep.

"Sort of," said Karen, kissing the baby, and softly reciting the larcenous jingle over to herself. That's what boys were deep down underneath, she said to herself, snips and snails and puppy dogs' tails, and, most of all, knaves of hearts. She thought she liked this knavishness of theirs.

She finished off the song very quietly in order not to waken Kristin again:

> The Knave of Hearts took back those tarts,
> And swore he'd steal no more.

"Vowed, Karen! Vowed!" said the sleepy little precisian, half-angrily. "Say vowed!"

"Vowed," said Karen.

Yes, vowed was better. She liked vowed. Sleepy herself at last, Karen blew a kiss to future vowings. Snips and snails and puppy dogs' tails. And Knaves of Hearts. And Vikings?

Shuttered again against the coming cold, the little beach house waited. The chimney was still warm. An owl and a red-headed woodpecker blundered down the flue into the dark living room and, perched on the backs of chairs, sat eying one another in the growing chill.

CHAPTER THREE

Indian Summer

INDIAN summer is hardly a reprieve from winter. It is a snare and a delusion, a ritual immolation, a final smoldering pyre of leaves and late blooming flowers. It seems to smoke a pipe of peace, but actually it is as suddenly treacherous as a painted brave on the warpath. Nevertheless, even though he quoted the old Vergilian proverb about 'ware of the Greeks when they come bearing gifts, Professor Desmond thought he might as well take advantage of this brief November respite. Might as well? Might much better!

In point of fact, he really had an excellent excuse, and, more to the point, an unexpended departmental grant to finance this modest scholar's junket of his. One of his graduate students, who taught the primary grades in a grammar school on the Cattaraugus Reservation, had turned up what appeared to be a genuine Indian analogue, still alive on the lips of an old tribal teller of tales, of the *Bear's Son* motif from the *Béowulf*. Folklorists had always assumed that this was a purely European wonder motif, originating somewhere in the north of Europe. If so, it must have been transmitted to the tale-tellers of the Five Nations by some European. But when? And how? Very, very long ago, the chances were. The question was: just how long ago? For an audacious hypothesis presented itself. Could it be a Viking relique? It was most suggestive, in this connection, that one of the uglier tribal names on the Cattaraugus Reservation was Big Swede.

The American Folklore people had informed him, when he

presented the analogue for certification, that a Canadian folklorist had recently discovered a *Bear's Son* variant on Christian Island two hundred and thirty miles due north from Buffalo in Georgian Bay, which was the very heart of the old Huron country. Story telling was absolutely tabu for Indians in spring, summer, and the early fall. The animals were listening then, and the *Pau-puk-Keewis*, the little Indian gods, who were so much like European goblins. When the last harvests were in, the animals and the *Keewis* slept. November, then, was a propitious month for folk tale collectors among the descendants of the ancient Iroquois.

Too, it would be relaxing to tool along the smooth Ontario highways. Jack's and Ellen's wedding had been emotionally taxing. Not physically, though, nor financially. It was the father of the bride who had to foot the bills, and the mother of the bride who did the leg work for that stickler for protocol, the saffron-robed god, Hymen. His turn would come later — his and Toby's. As the father of four daughters, the marriage bell would most likely toll a knell for his pocketbook no less than three and, quite possibly, four times. But he did not intend to anticipate that day.

Professor Desmond put the pencil which he had used to record the starting mileage back into his breast pocket, straightened the red capped elf on the mirror reflector, loosened his tie, and opened the door beside him.

"Hop in, Moira," he said.

Moira was going on the trip with him for three good reasons. For one thing, it was her turn. For another, Armistice Day falling on Monday and a Teachers' Convention on Friday meant no time lost for her at school. For still another, he was driving into Indian country, and Moira was custodian of Indian *mystique* in the Desmond household. On Halloween, for the third year running, she had won the prize for the best Indian in the Firehouse competition.

On the Canadian side of the Peace Bridge the green Chevrolet turned right instead of the customary left. Left lay the little beach house on Lake Erie. Right lay Toronto, Lake Ontario, and Georgian Bay. As the car struck inland, Professor Desmond fell again to thinking on his *Bear's Son* problem. The purest *Bear's Son* analogues were to be found in old Northern literature — in the *Béowulf*, and in the Sagas. He wondered if there could be anything in the theory that the Vikings had made their way into Ontario — either in Leif's or Thorfinn's day or, three centuries after, in the day of Paal the son of Knut whose Greenland expedition, if the Kensington Stone people were correct, got as far as Minnesota a whole hundred years and more before Columbus.

Midland, where there was a shrine to the Jesuit martyrs, lay some thirty miles off their route on a high tableland that dominated the surrounding countryside. But Professor Desmond wanted Moira to see it. As a matter of fact, he was anxious to see it again himself. He had a strong sense of Vergilian *pietas*, of rapport with the beautiful North American continent on which he lived. Surely the ancients had been right. There was a numinous presence, a *genius loci*, in every lake, in every wood, in every tree, even. It was what a medieval philosopher had called the *thisness*, and a modern poet the *inscape*, of things. These lesser gods were born of morning and evening; of sky and water; of earth and tree. They went with unshod feet down the forest trails. One felt the cool wind of their passing best when one was alone — or else when one was with a chosen comrade such as the little pig-tailed girl by his side. The *numen* moved then, and the imagination bowed. Without a human eye to worship or record, the holy circle could not be closed. Or rather — for it was a triune, even a trinitarian experience — the sacred triangle could not be completed. The sacred triangle of place, man, and indwelling spirit. And the *numen* trembled closest of all to revelation in places like this Midland, where men had borne witness to the *numen* with their blood, where the cup of libation had been brimmed full from living human veins.

They lunched at Midland with better than an hour to spare, since Professor Desmond calculated they needed only another two hours' driving time to reach the cabin on Georgian Bay. In a little store on the grounds Moira bought three miniature binoculars for her sisters. One was colored red, one white, one blue. They were just the size to set on a doll house grand piano; and, if you looked through the right end, there was a picture of the martyrs inside. Professor Desmond bought four silver scapular medals.

The middle-aged Jesuit, whose task it was to bless the religious articles, looked through his spectacles at Professor Desmond.

"You must like scapulars in your house," said the priest.

"Quite to the contrary," said Professor Desmond, grinning back at the Jesuit. "My wife detests them. Hygienically speaking, that is. Not ideologically. She says the children insist on wearing them until they rot off. She says they are a part of Mediterranean Catholicism — which may or may not be picturesque in the Mediterranean. She says she will take Catholic theology, the Protestant ethic, and good old American hygiene. In short, she is a woman with a crotchet. That's why I'm getting scapular medals."

Then Professor Desmond remembered that, most likely, the priest was a Canadian.

"When I say good old American hygiene," he amended quickly, "I am referring, of course, to North American."

The Jesuit smiled again.

"You know," he said, after he had finished muttering the words of sacramental power over the medals, "I think your wife has something."

They left Midland a little after two o'clock. Beyond this point, the roads were not quite so good as the great trunk highways of Ontario on which they had been driving. But they were quite good enough. When it came to riding comfort, thought Professor Desmond, what was so rare as an Indian summer day in early November? The car seemed to run on purring cushions of air. There was nothing of the sultry closeness of July and August motoring which Kristin called the "hot railroad track smell."

The contour of the country began to change. Pines became general. Bare rock slashes appeared. Water flashed darkly through the trees: the dark, deep, still, cold, clear, clean water of the north country. Professor Desmond tried to recall exactly, so that he might quote them to Moira, Keats's mighty lines about the "moving waters at their priestlike task of pure ablution round earth's human shores."

My God! he said to himself. What lines! How they caught the healing, sacramental aspect of nature. He tried to explain it all to Moira, but she was thinking of something else.

"Who was the big priest, Dad?" she asked. "The one on the ceiling?"

"What ceiling?" said Professor Desmond.

"The church ceiling," said Moira.

"Oh, that one," said Professor Desmond, ransacking his memories. "That was Father Jean de Brébeuf. The Indians called him Echon. After they killed him at the stake, the Hurons drank his blood in order to make them as brave as he had been. He was a giant of a man."

"A real giant?" asked Moira.

Professor Desmond had to think for a moment or so.

"Realer than a real giant," he said finally, lighting a cigarette off the dashboard lighter.

The November sun was pleasantly warm within the Chevrolet's glassed-in aquarium. Outside, as the afternoon shadows began to lengthen, the Canadian ocean of air took on a tang of the Arctic. The car's slight rocking motion made Moira feel a little sleepy. She put her head back on the plaid seat cover. Professor Desmond glanced down at the blonde hair framing the flushed child face. He yawned. Then, settling back into the seat, he drew on his cigarette.

Joe Bourdon was waiting for them at the landing. Joe was half Chippewa. His father had been a Frenchman — not a descendant of the Canadian *voyageurs*, however. He had come from France on a cattleboat with some Basque herders, landed at the port of New York, made his way to Washington, D. C., and there married a Chippewa girl. The Bourdon boys, Joe and his younger brother Louis, both as Indians and as Frenchmen one generation removed from the Norman countryside, found a better outlet for their particular skills in the Indian country of Ontario than in the United States. The move did not much impair their power of mobility. By international agreement, as members of the Indian Treaty Nations, they could go back and forth across the border with no questions asked. They could fish, hunt, and trap without license. The only license they had to pay for was the celluloid button they wore pinned to their hats certifying them as professional guides; and there were no better guides in all Canada. During the winters they worked in a Georgian Bay saw mill.

Joe Bourdon had married a white woman and lived near Honey Harbor. Louis was married to a full-blooded Chippewa. Louis and his wife lived on Christian Island and spoke Chippewa in preference to English. Mrs. Bourdon's mother, who lived with them, knew nothing but Chippewa.

Joe was squat, bronzed, and taciturn. Sitting there cross-legged under the glassed-in cabin of his launch, he looked like a Buddha. Joe's services came high: twenty dollars a day, and whatever whiskey his clients were willing to let him consume. But he was worth it. He could find bear, deer — moose, even, in a moose year — partridge, pheasant, and whatever fish happened to be in season. Professor Desmond had known Joe for twenty-five years. He did not seem to have changed one bit over those two decades and a half. One could not even tell if his hair had grayed, since Joe never seemed to take his hat off.

"Your daughter?" said Joe, gesturing with his cigarette. It was much more a statement than a question.

Professor Desmond knew the premium Joe placed on children; how he felt that fatherhood fulfilled a man. He felt absurdly pleased.

"My daughter Moira," said Professor Desmond expansively.

"She look Indian," said Joe.

Professor Desmond, who had had the same idea more than once, was a little startled at the guide's utter seriousness. By George, standing next to Joe, she did look Indian, for all her blonde hair and blue eyes. The high, flat cheekbones helped. So did the straight back. And, come to think of it, there was some tradition in the family of an Indian ancestor on Toby's mother's side. Maybe it was no accident that Moira always carried off the prize for Indians on Halloween. He tried to remember what it was he had heard about Toby's ancestor.

"Way back, Joe," he said. "Potawatomi, I think."

Joe looked hard and long.

"No Potawatomi," he said with finality. "Chippewa. Maybe Huron, too. But Chippewa, for sure."

"Oh, come now, Joe," said Professor Desmond, laughing. "The Indian blood, if any, goes back a hundred years. How can you tell after a century?"

Joe Bourdon had known Professor Desmond since the Professor was a boy. He stared at him impassively.

"I can tell," he said, after a time. "You say in letter you come this time to track old story among Indians back many hundred years. How can you tell story after many centuries? Blood easier to tell than story."

It was a shrewd argument; and behind it was the unspoken accusation that to the white man all Indians looked alike. Professor Desmond did not object further. Instead, he helped Joe transfer the bags from the car to the launch. Then, locking the car, he steadied Moira while she stepped over the high gunwale into the back of the boat. The cabin they had rented was on one of the shores of Go Home Bay, near the flat rocks where pike trolling was best. One could get there only by boat.

As they rounded the last headland before the little landing pier, the sun was just setting. The air stayed fresh and delicate as early morning, during the brief northern dusk. By the time Joe and Professor Desmond had finished unrolling the duffle bags, it was already dark; and, of a sudden, very cold. The Indian knelt and touched a match to the dry tinder under the logs in the fireplace. Professor Desmond set the coffee pot on the stove. Kindling-wood fires worked quick. Soon shadows were leaping on the rough-hewn walls. On the wood-burning stove coffee began to hiss and bubble, and the pot to dance.

Moira had gone out on the screened sleeping porch which overlooked the dark water of the inlet. Almost timorously, she breathed in the cold air. Then she took huge gulps. It was sharp in her lungs. A single star poised over a pine tip on the further shore. Suddenly, a half mile or so across the water, rang out a wild operatic cadence; inhuman, but strangely human, too. It had no words, but it was eloquent of savage, hopeless, elemental dismay. A ululant echo gave back the unearthly scream. Moira started. A hand was laid on her arm.

"Do not be afraid, little Chippewa," said old Joe Bourdon soothingly. "It is only a loon. No more."

Only a loon? It was the soul of the northern wilderness astray in some purgatory of air and rock and water. Moira heard it three more times before she fell asleep; and each time it shocked her anew. Joe and Professor Desmond stayed up a little longer, chatting and smoking. Before ten o'clock they, too, turned in, first latching the screen and carefully banking the log fire. The moon had set.

Overhead in the sky the northern lights burned and crackled. Waking once, and raising herself on her elbow, Moira watched the colored streamers dance over the tops of the pines. The luminous dial of her father's traveling clock read midnight. In a little while she was asleep again.

The good weather held over Saturday. They fished all morning and afternoon. Louis Bourdon turned up to talk to them round about eleven in his own launch which was trimmer and faster than his brother's. They were fishing off a rock skerry at the time. When Louis hove to, Joe tied a large rock to his painter, tossed this primitive anchor onto the skerry, and all four of them clambered ashore for lunch.

Like Joe, Louis took a long hard look at Moira. Then he said something to his brother in French. Joe nodded, a satisfied smile on his bronzed face.

"Louis think girl look Indian, too," he said to Professor Desmond.

Louis said something else to Joe in French. Professor Desmond, who thought he knew French quite well, was not precisely at home in this woodsman's *patois*. Listening carefully, he caught what seemed to be the unfamiliar word, *orenda*, uttered three or four times. He took it that *orenda* was generic Iroquois for something or other which Moira appeared either to have or be. This time, when Louis finished speaking, Joe looked a trifle worried.

"What does Louis think of Moira, Joe?" asked Professor Desmond, not stopping in his fishing.

"He say she good girl," said Joe uneasily.

Maybe Louis had. Professor Desmond saw no reason to doubt Joe's statement. Louis had also said she was or had *orenda*. Professor Desmond returned to the attack.

"Joe," he said. "What does *orenda* mean?"

Joe shrugged. A shutter seemed to come down over his face.

"It something to do with Great Spirit," he said, dismissing the subject. "Indian word. Bourdons Christian now. No longer have to do with old gods."

Then, as Professor Desmond continued to look baffled, Joe relented a little.

"Do not worry, John," he said. "*Orenda* old Indian thing. But good. Mean good thing."

Lunch was a very good thing indeed. There was really only one way to eat fish, Professor Desmond thought lazily, leaning back against a sun-warmed boulder, and cradling a third big cup of coffee in his mittened hands. Catch them yourself, keep them alive in a pail of water, knock them on the head, gut and bone them, then broil and bread them without delay. Joe and Louis were past masters at the art. Squatting over the fire they had made in a rock hollow, they seemed to perform the complicated operation in a single fluid gesture. And with immemorial dignity, too. They did everything with this same graceful economy of motion. Even to rolling a cigarette. Professor Desmond watched Joe dust out the tobacco from his leather pouch, run a flickering tongue over the seam, roll the small white cylinder between two fingers, balance the white tube between head and ear, to be held in reserve, and roll another for immediate consumption. Then, lighting the tobacco tube, he blew a cloud of smoke luxuriously through his nostrils.

Moira, huddled against another rock, swaddled in a blanket, had her own thoughts. Though Louis had not yet spoken to her, not even when he handed over a golden-grilled fish, Moira thought she liked him even better than Joe. He looked more Indian somehow. Like the Magua in The Last of the Mohicans. Except, of course, that he was a nice Magua, and did not have his face white-striped for the warpath.

A late flight of ducks went over, flying very high. A hawk circled the place where Joe had tossed the fish heads. Seduced by the gold light, a chipmunk flashed, chattering, down a bare tree bole that had, decades before, been riven by lightning. Out in the dark waters of Go Home Bay it was very still, except for a slight splash now and again, when a large bass surfaced. The sun, riding high, was still quite warm. But there was a growing chill in the air. Beating his gloved hands together, Louis looked toward the north.

"Big snow coming," he said, speaking in English for the first time. "Late tonight maybe. Early tomorrow for sure. Indian Summer over by midnight. Professor Desmond should clear up business tonight. Tomorrow too late."

"It's O.K. with me," said Professor Desmond. "If the story woman is ready."

"She ready," said Louis. "I can take you over to Christian Island tonight. Then Joe can call in morning for return trip to Honey Harbor. Early in morning, though."

"What about Moira?" asked Professor Desmond. "I don't want her sitting up all night on Christian Island. And, quite obviously, I can't leave her alone back in the cabin."

"Easy," said Louis. "She can stay with my wife on Christian Island. I think she like it fine."

"What say, Moira?" said Professor Desmond a trifle anxiously, for he knew her innate shyness.

"Oh, yes," said Moira. "I'd like that."

So it was settled. After another hour of fishing, they picked up anchor and chugged off. Louis Bourdon stopped his boat at the cabin for the Desmond pajamas and toothbrushes. Professor Desmond slipped a pad of scratch paper and two sharpened pencils into the pocket of his windbreaker. Moira packed her birthday present copy of C. S. Lewis' *The Lion, the Witch and the Wardrobe* in case she found it hard to fall asleep in the Bourdon cabin. Then they were off for Christian Island in Louis' launch. It was agreed that Joe should call for them next morning at six.

The Georgian Bay November sunset was a conflagration of pastels: of mauves and violets shading into deeper purples; of rose-dust clouds drifting across a pale moon — a moon that seemed as startling as only a moon can seem when glimpsed in daylight. Then the colors were gone and the sky was a clear well of apple-green. A single star pricked out over Christian Island.

"*Che-n-an-goh*," said Louis Bourdon, pointing with his cigarette. "Great Star. Good luck to see so soon."

Like many professors of the humanities Professor Desmond was awed by astro-physics.

"It is a world larger than ours," he said with an enthusiasm that mitigated his pedantry. "It is a blazing sun for other earths."

Louis Bourdon inclined his head ever so slightly as if in deference to the other's superior knowledge.

"So I have heard in school," he said courteously. "But I do not know if I really believe it. To me *Che-n-an-goh* is more like one of the old gods. Or else more like this little girl here. In either case, more like a person than a thing. In Indian we should call your daughter N-an-gohs. Little Star."

He nodded to Moira.

"Remember that, little one," he said, smiling. "In Chippewa you have been called N-an-gohs. Little Star. It is a compliment for a queen."

Moira crimsoned with pleasure. Never had she felt so complimented. It was as if a great noble praised her.

Professor Desmond was still dreaming.

"Just think, Louis," he said, sweeping his arm in a large circle round the horizon into which other stars had now begun to break. "Man is on the very edge of the conquest of space. If you and I do not live to see it, Moira may. How would you like to be the first man to climb out of a space ship onto that star? To conquer — what did you call it?"

There was a little smile on Louis Bourdon's lips. Moira felt almost embarrassed for her father.

"To conquer Che-n-an-goh?" said Louis Bourdon. "No, my friend, I do not think I like that. Perhaps to make a pilgrimage there. To pray there. Yes, I like that, maybe. But conquer — no."

Louis Bourdon tossed his cigarette in a tiny hissing arc through the pine-sharp air. It was almost dark now.

"You know," he said. "I think white men think too much of conquering. They are great conquerors, yes. But it is their limitation."

The boat nosed in alongside the landing pier, one side grinding against the planked walk and sunken piles. An Indian woman was waiting on the dock. Louis Bourdon flung her the painter. She made it fast to a wooden bollard.

"My wife, Marie," he said to Moira and Professor Desmond.

He pronounced her name in the French fashion which, to Moira's ear, made it sound all the more Indian.

Marie bowed.

"My friends," said Louis Bourdon. "Professor Desmond and N-an-gohs. Little Star."

Again Moira felt that unexpected flush of pleasure. It was as if, without warning, she had begun to grow up. As if she were a person now, not just a child.

It was very cozy in the Bourdon house, after her father and Louis Bourdon had gone. Moira did not feel strange at all, even though the wrinkled old woman, who was Mrs. Bourdon's mother and who didn't know any English, looked like no one she had ever known, unless it could be the Lapland Woman or the Finland Woman in Andersen's *Snow Queen*. The old woman sat on one side of the blazing fire, sewing on a gay rag rug and smiling at the child. She said something in Chippewa to her daughter which, of course, Moira could not understand, though she thought she caught the strange word, *orenda*, spoken more than once; and, just after it, what sounded to her like *okee*. She did not really suppose, however, that it was *okee*.

The walls were whitewashed and very clean. A silver crucifix, which old Bourdon had brought from France, hung over the mantel. An Ingersoll clock ticked fat, comfortable ticks in the quiet. Moira opened *The Lion, the Witch and the Wardrobe* to the place where Tumnus, the faun, told the human children how in Narnia, since the coming of the White Witch, it was always winter and never Christmas. It had never occurred to her before, but it was true. Christmas was a kind of summer in the midst of winter; an Indian summer of the heart. It would be a dreadful thing always to have winter and never Christmas.

Moira's head began to nod. Both Indian women looked like witches to her now in her drowsing state — but good witches, not bad ones like the White Witch of Narnia. There was a dry rustling sound like the scratching of little nails on the window. It sounded like snow, but, of course, it couldn't be snow. It was too early in the year for that. One of the Indian women — she thought it was the old one, but couldn't be sure — gave her a fragrant smelling cup of what seemed to be tea. Moira had never drunk tea before, only milk, but, under the circumstances, she thought it must be all right. It would not be polite to refuse. It tasted delicious, too. She handed back the cup. The old lady patted her on the braids. She felt very, very sleepy.

Hours later, it must have been, she awoke. She was in her nightgown, sleeping on a low couch opposite the fireplace. Louis Bourdon was in the room. He beat what seemed to be snow out of his mackinac.

"The big snow has begun," he said to his wife in Chippewa. "We had it in our face all the way back to our dock. They will have to leave in two hours at the latest, if they are to ride out the storm. I have given Professor Desmond our room. Why have you put the child to bed here, and not on the cot in the room with her father?"

Marie looked strangely at her husband.

"Perhaps it was wrong," she said to him. "But I gave her the witch drink. She is more than *orenda* even. She is what, in the old time, they called *oki*. Mother saw it at once."

Louis Bourdon seized his wife's arm with suppressed passion.

"You did very wrong," he said between clenched teeth. "Have not the priests told us that only One of all those born of man is really *oki*? She is *orenda*, yes. That is good. It is also dangerous. Why did you give her the drink?"

It was Marie's turn to look frightened.

"I do not know," she said pleadingly, beginning to cry. "I could not help it. I have never known anyone before who was so much *orenda* as this child. It was for her, too, more than for us. She should have her chance. She may never have it again. Would you not want a chance, if you were *orenda*? It cannot hurt her, if we are wrong. And, if we are right, when she awakes, she will forget anyway. But her blood will remember."

Moira raised herself on one elbow.

"What is *oki*, Louis?" she asked.

"*Oki*, child?" said Louis Bourdon. "Why — "

But Marie, in her turn, had taken him by the arm.

"Listen, Louis," she said, almost stammering in her excitement. "Listen! The child is speaking Chippewa! Was I not right?"

Louis Bourdon began to sweat.

"*Mon dieu!*" he said, relapsing into French. "I do not know. It is so dangerous. Now she goes back in time — who knows how far? Perhaps as far, even, as her father wants to go. Back to the Bear's Son and the men in winged helmets."

No. Not quite so far as that. But very far, nonetheless. And in time alone, not space. In space the child was still on the shores of Georgian Bay, but a short paddle's distance from Christian Island. Only she did not think of it as Georgian Bay, but as the Lake of the Hurons. At the beginning she was still Moira Desmond. Then things got mixed, and she seemed to be both Moira Desmond and N-an-gohs, a Chippewa boy. Suddenly she was N-an-gohs, and no one else. It was very cold. Before dawn it would come on to snow.

The time had come at last! No later than the morrow N-an-gohs, Little Star, would be Che-n-an-goh, Great Star, the star he had seen rise in the morning east during his four-day manhood fast. He had seen it also in the dream each warrior's *manitou* grants him as he watches on the threshold of life, waiting to step over into the lodge where the men of the tribe sit in council. Little Star's hunchbacked uncle, the great sorcerer Tonneraouanont, had not liked this matter of the star dream. Not at all. If his nephew were to succeed him as medicine man of the Bear nation, by rights he should have dreamed of a serpent. Maybe, though, on second thought, the star was all right, too. Tonneraouanont who, because he had no children of his own, looked on Little Star as his son, had said the star of his dream was the North star, which the people of the Iroquois called the Bear star. Three hunter stars followed the Bear star through summer skies with their keen arrows. In the month of the Hunting Moon their star arrowheads found the Bear's heart; and his blood dripped red onto the autumn leaves. Probably Tonneraouanont was right. Tonneraouanont was usually right. It must have been the Bear star. For his part, though, Little Star could have sworn it was the Morning Star, instead. In either case it was fitting that he wear, as talisman, the moonstone on a deer thong round his neck. His fingers sought the smooth round stone and were reassured.

Anyway, it did not matter much. On the morrow he, Little Star, would become Great Star, after he had killed Echon, the giant priest who brought bad medicine to the Hurons. Little Star crooned over to himself the song he would sing aloud, for the first and last time, while his white foe lay dying. The gods of night had given it to him, in his long winter watch, and he was grateful:

I go forth as the bear that is great in courage.
I go forth as the mountain lion that moves noiseless in the snow.
Listen, Echon! Listen, great priest! Listen, Frenchman!
You walk the wood trail to the Darkening Land.

I have come to cover you with the black leaves of death.
Listen, Echon, enemy of my people!
Tonight the Great Spirit shall drink thy blood!

As he waited there in the still cold that locked the earth fast in the month of the Winter Moon, Little Star shifted from foot to foot on the hard-beaten snow outside of Echon's bark lodge. Yes, tonight, soon after midnight, Echon would die, and tomorrow there would be a forty-kettle feast in the lodges of the Bear nation. Everything lay in readiness. The bow was made of seasoned hickory. The magic arrow of flint had been shaped into wicked life over Tonneraouanont's fire, and, deadly flat as the diamond head of a swamp adder, fitted to its shaft in the sorcerer's lodge on the lonely headland that thrust into the bay just to the north of Ihonatiria, chief city of the Bear nation. They had made strong medicine there together last night, he and Tonneraouanont, by the red gleam of the wizard's pitch-pine logs. Together they had cast scraped porcupine bones into the hot ashes. Together had they danced the whirling dance of the Masks, and the even wilder dance of the *Otakrendoiae*. Together had they called upon the age-old *Atisken*, the great dead who had once lived along the wooded shores of this mighty Huron lake, and who now, in their turn, danced the dance of the Dead in the wheeling northern lights. Even as Little Star crouched there in the cold, the *Atisken* were dancing this same dance of theirs this very night. The colored streamers of light crackled and shifted over Echon's ridge pole. Little Star raised a clenched fist to them in greeting.

Last night, for the first time, Tonneraouanont had whispered into Little Star's ear the name of the demon, *Aoutaerohi*; and that of the white panther, *Ontarraoura*. He had told him of *Iouskeha*, the Sky Boy, giver of the wheat, keeper of the beasts; *Iouskeha* whose frugal bounty the white spoilers soiled and profaned. Then he bade him cast tobacco on the fire to *Oatarra*, the little doll with the dreadful face. As the acrid smoke bellied out into the lodge, Tonneraouanont told the coughing Little Star that he, Tonneraouanont, was the greatest sorcerer the Bears had ever known, but that Little Star might be fated to go beyond even him and to become *oki*; that is, one with the wood gods. Squatting in the dark and cold outside the bark house where Echon made ready for the white man's Christmas feast, Little Star shivered at the very thought. And from ecstasy, not from cold. Not even the great Echon, whom Little Star would shortly kill and, after, eat his roasted heart — not even Echon was *oki*. No later than the morrow's dawn Tonneraouanont would receive the new warrior into the ranks of the *Arendiowane*, the wielders of power. And, after that, perhaps — who knew? — to be *oki!*

It was growing much, much colder. Like a warrior in white buckskins, the winter moon strode across the heavens. Little Star could hear the pine trees cracking in the cold. His breath came and went white in the brightness of the night. It formed little ice stars on the beaver collar about his neck. The chill air cut his lungs like a knife. His nostrils stiffened. He wriggled the leaden toes in his moccasins and stamped his feet, in their deer leggings, up and down on the snow crust. It was the white time of year when the Great Spirit took the form of a white Hare even as, in fall, He took the form of a red Fox. The northern lights had finally stopped their dancing now. Now winter stars' cold fire blazed over the ridge pole of the bark house the Hurons had built for Echon. Other stars burned like lonely council fires above the dark pines which stood straight and tall and silent, scouts in the waiting night.

Yes. The waiting night. The word was well chosen. Never had Little Star breathed and felt a night so full of expectancy as this one. It was almost as if the sky and air were *oki*. What did they wait on, these watching trees and stars? What did they watch for, these waiting stars and trees? Little Star fingered the star-stone beneath his furs. Stooping, he picked a pine needle from the snow and, cupping his hands, rolled the needle back and forth between two palms till the bruised fragrance made a sharp point of delicacy in the dark and cold. The stars, his brothers, would approve of the wordless sacrifice. Pine needles shared somehow in the star nature. Did not the blue-green star-rayed needles shine with a star's remote cool light even at midday? The stars, his brothers, were sons of the great sun, and brothers of their sister moon. Shining creatures moved and had their being in them. Little Star raised a silent prayer to his star brothers:

> Morning star, Evening star, North star, all stars,
> I call on you for help against Echon, my enemy.

A bell rang out in the water-clear night. Little Star, listening, counted twelve strokes. This bell was new. It had come over the great water in one of the monstrous war canoes of the *Agnonka*, the iron men who, in their own tongue, called themselves the French. Before the coming of the bell, Echon used to strike a copper kettle hanging in a tree. As the last stroke of the new bell thrummed away into the white stillness, those Hurons who honored Echon's medicine and followed the thoughts he read aloud out of his talking bark came walking through the night from their lodges in Ihonatiria. With anger and contempt Little Star watched them go, under the crimson cross totem, into the candlelit sweetness, fragrant with fir and cedar, with silvered birch and dried Indian grass, of the giant priest's chapel. Working with his own strong hands Echon had shaped the cross totem. With his own hands sharpened deer bones to nail points to hold the cross bars straight. With his own hands painted the cross red. It was this same cross which, above all else, accounted for Tonneraouanont's implacable enmity against Echon. More even than the weather vane on Echon's roof, and the witch which lived in his French clock, Tonneraouanont hated this scarlet wood. Was it not the reason why, last summer, his incantations had for the first time failed to bring the life-bearing rain? Because the Thunder Bird, who spoke from the clouds, and the Turkey Cock of the lightning feared the blood-red wood that flaunted over Ihonatiria?

On his own side, Little Star had other quite different reasons for hating Echon. Echon was a white man, one of the evil wasters who made the pine woods ring with their murderous thunder sticks. True, he carried no thunder stick himself, only his golden cup and his talking bark that fluttered, when you opened it — as Little Star, to his great fright, had once done — like poplar leaves before rain. But he was the priest of those who carried the wanton killing irons. Indians killed for flesh and pelts, but not as white men killed. When an Indian killed a deer, even before feathering his shaft he begged the noble animal's pardon. He knew it was his own blood he spilled, not just the deer's. Afterward, with exact and loving hand, he pictured the deer in beads and paint — not as his quarry merely, either, but as his brother and his friend. But the white ravager had no sense of piety about the woods and streams. Already the fish in their countless thousands were fewer; and the pheasants and the wood cock.

Already the fox and beaver grew harder to trap. Already the great bear, the brother of the Bear nation, could be found only on the mountaintop.

When, last night, singing his song to the devil, *Io, Sechongnac,* Tonneraouanont had again flung tobacco on the fire and the flames flared up and sank once more, the sorcerer had shown Little Star terrible pictures in the embers. There had been wars and rumors of wars, the red man dying in the smoke of battle, the white invader triumphant everywhere. But good warriors took their chances in battle. Worst of all had been the death of the beasts. The Great Spirit would no longer endure it. Echon must die. Little Star touched the thumb and index finger of his right hand to the bow string he kept hidden beneath his furs. Then, in the rear of the last stragglers, he, too, walked, under the shadow of the red cross, into Echon's bark house of arched saplings lashed together.

Never had he been inside the great priest's lodge before — the time he touched the talking bark, he had come upon the book on a bench outside the lodge. In the third room, warm now not only with the breath of many worshipers but with the spicy scent of the incense Echon burned to his god instead of good Huron tobacco, stood the little chapel framed with fresh-cut fir and cedar branches. Little Star's sensitive nostrils twitched. It was a queer sort of medicine Echon made here. One not at all unpleasing to the nose and eye. Tonneraouanont's lodge smelt of death; of old bones and moldering animal flesh. Echon's house, even on this winter night, smelt of springtide life. Never before had the young warrior seen trees borne into a house except to burn. It was as if the spruce boughs lived a new life in Echon's house. The fir needles, too, gained a new brilliance and a new pungency in the mellow candle warmth.

Little Star's fringed legging caught in some low-set branches. Looking down, he saw that the branches fenced, as with a forest palisade, a clump of tiny images grouped about a sleeping baby doll. The little wooden people all had Huron faces and wore cunningly woven Indian clothes. Further back among the evergreens stiffly stood toy deer and bear. There had been a squaw's hand at work here. Little Star looked disdainfully at the stiff little group. Stepping back with all the arrogance of a brave who scorned woman's work, he disentangled his buckskin legging. He had heard of the child god,

Iesous, before. And here he was in all his foolish helplessness, no
larger than — not even so large as, really — the doll, Oatarra. True,
Iesous had not Oatarra's dreadful face. His sleeping little face was
lovable; brown and smooth as an acorn. But, anyway, what did a
god with a baby's face? Ought not a god look terrible? And could a
warrior kneel to a child? Here was his mother, too. Did warriors pay
high honor to squaws? Little Star spat into the evergreens.

Then, quite suddenly, he started. It was a trick of the unsteady
candlelight, of course. Nevertheless, the little corncob face of the
lady, Mary, dark and shining as it was with the sunflower oil the
Huron artist had lavished on it, made him think of the gentle
Chippewa woman who had been his mother. Little Star had loved
his mother. When the time came round for naming the new man
child, she had called him by the Chippewa name for star instead of
by the rougher tongue of his father who, only a year before the boy's
birth, had taken the Chippewa woman in a raid. She lay now, rotten
in death, wrapped in a skin bag on her pitiful little scaffolding of
poles, waiting till the flesh fell away and the bones, the holy Atisken,
were bare; waiting till spring when the great Huron Feast of the
Dead would set her free to walk the last trail to the place where the
dead of her tribe — not Little Star's, alas — would receive her. Sadly
Little Star said over to himself the cry of the souls: "H-a-e-e! H-a-e-e!"
Even as he mourned the mother he would never see again, Little
Star's dark sinewy hand relaxed somewhat on the bow. But the
guiding finger did not desert the string.

The service had already progressed some distance on its appointed
way. Echon was not wearing the usual cumbrous black robe he had
to tuck up high whenever he got into a canoe. Tonight he had on a
white robe with a red sash and, around his tree trunk of a muscle-
columned neck, a crimson scarf. Now, just as Little Star moved
soundless to a point of vantage squarely opposite the giant priest,
Echon closed the talking bark that told him how to sing his songs,
and, coming forward before the squatting Hurons, raised his hand
in Huron greeting. Then, in his harsh white man's voice, he began
to tell of Iesous in the tongue of the red men who listened.

"In the name of our Father," he began, "and of His Son, and of
Their Holy Spirit — whom you of the Ouendats know as the Great
Spirit — greetings on this holy night. Tonight Iesous, son of the

Great Spirit, born as a Little Spirit to the maid, Mary, is born also in the hearts of the Hurons, of the warriors and the mothers of the great Bear nation. Listen to my good news, red brothers. For I bring you those good tidings of great joy brought first to earth by the shining star people whose right name is angels. I speak truth. My words are straight, not crooked like arrows flawed in the making. As the wise men of your people say: *I hold my word tight to my breast.*"

Little Star's hand closed in quick anger round the smooth-rubbed flint head. The giant priest lied. The shining star folk, Little Star's brothers, had nothing to do with Echon's god. Nor was there any Little Spirit, either, only a Great One. And the Great Spirit was the red man's god, not the god of the white man. Let the white man keep his foolish gods to himself. He knew of one arrow not flawed in the making, Little Star grimly told himself. Groping under his furs, he bent the supple bow and, without removing the muffling beaver pelt, sighted along the polished shaft straight at Echon's heart.

Almost as if he could read Little Star's mind, the giant priest began again:

"It is true that the Frenchman has a white skin and the Huron a red. That the French way is different from the Huron way. That there are as many different ways of doing and saying things as there are peoples on the earth. But there is not one Great Spirit for the Frenchman and another for the Huron. There is only one God for all nations. His image is stamped on our faces, red and white alike. He is our Father. In Him Huron and Frenchman are brothers, different in skin, one in *esken* — in immortal soul. In Him we live again, you and I, in the land of the holy *Atisken*, where we shall look once more on the living faces of our well loved dead. And tonight the Great Spirit's son, the Little Star, is born in Bethlehem of Juda, which is far off across the great water, but which is also here, in the hearts of the Bear nation."

The Little Star! *N-an-gohs!* It was his own name as his Chippewa mother had sung it to him, she whose remembered face was like the face of Iesous' mother! The poet in Little Star looked with respect on Echon. His bow hand allowed the string to slack. Let Echon have his say out. Truly, evil though he was, he was also a mighty speaker. And he gave tongue to the great hope Little Star had never even dared to voice that, in the far off country of the *Atisken*, he would greet his mother once again. A white peace of the heart began to fall like snow on Little Star.

"This night, behold," said Echon, "is created a new heaven and a new earth. For unto us a Child is born, a little chieftain, God, our brother. And his name shall be called the Prince of Peace. The fox and the deer shall couch together. The mountain lion and the buffalo lie down in the same lodge. The great bear shall put his paw in his Huron brother's hand. Dust shall choke the mouth of the evil *oki*, the Great Serpent. The good *oki* shall bruise the Great Serpent's head. Men shall beat their lances into plowshares. They shall not hurt nor kill in all my holy mountain, saith the Lord our Father. They shall not stumble in the darkness, for the Little Day Star shall light their halting steps."

Little Star began to growl deep in his throat. Under his robe, he slipped the deer-thong back into its notch. Echon knew not whereof he spoke. One, at least, should yet stumble on the dark trail that led to the Darkening Land. One who slandered Tonneraouanont's *oki*, the Great Serpent. Yet, truly, Echon must be as great a sorcerer as Tonneraouanont himself. For, almost in spite of himself, Little Star found scant anger in his heart at this latest sacrilege. A second time the hand on the bowstring went limp and nerveless. Dreamily, summoning his last reserves of resolution, Little Star hummed over to himself his death song against Echon:

"*You walk the wood trail to the Darkening Land.*
I have come to cover you with the black leaves of death.
Listen, Echon, enemy of my people!
Tonight the Great Spirit shall drink thy blood!"

Echon had a song, too. A song of life against the dark trails of death. Putting down the golden cup from which he had just drunk the blood of the Great Spirit, and wiping his bearded lips with a piece of snowy white linen, the giant priest raised one powerful hand. Then, from the bronzed throats of Echon's Huron chorus burst the thunder of Echon's *Carol of the Huron Nation* that put into the tongue of the Bears the good news the star people had sung to men one far-off night in Palestine.

Ouarie onnaouakoueton ndio sen tsatonnharonnion
  Iesous ahatonnia!
So the angels tell their glad Gospel:
Mary has borne the Great Spirit!
This holy morn is Jesus born!

The last thundering chorus trailed off into a silence broken only by a pine needle tinkling on the earthen floor of Echon's lodge. Then three tall chieftains, crowned with eagle feathers and in the ceremonial robes of council, came forward to the crib, bearing strings of wampum and glistening peltries in their hands. Candlelight shone on the dark intent faces. Echon's voice rang out again in a strong Huron cry.

"Behold!" he called, and the lodge was full of his voice. "The chiefs of the Bear nation bear gifts to the Infant Chief!"

Behind the chiefs came other Hurons. Men and women, and little children, too, their hands loaded down with offerings. Pemmican, dried corn, furs of the fox and beaver, wild turkey feathers woven into a tiny head-dress for the Babe, beads, small moccasins, sweet-smelling grasses plaited into ropes.

Little Star, watching, felt a slow, fierce exultancy mount in his heart. Carefully he set the bow down and aside, away from the feet of the worshipers, down on the beaten floor. The combat was over. Echon had won. And Little Star, in his heart of hearts, was glad. He would still defend the Great Spirit — to the death, if necessary. But he knew now that hunchbacked Tonneraouanont was wrong. Echon was a friend, not a foe of the Great Spirit. And the Little Spirit! Why had no one told the people of the Bear about the Little Spirit?

The poet in Little Star sang for joy. The star of his dream had not been the Bear Star at all, as Tonneraouanont had insisted. Here before him, lying in a mimic crib, was the star of his dream. Here was what had been missing when he walked the hills on snowshoes, and sang of the land he loved. The land itself had an *esken* now. No longer was the Great Spirit far off, unapproachable. He was here and now and always, sleeping in an Indian cradle with an adorable Huron face. The lost was found, the missing restored. This Virgin, with the remembered face of the Chippewa woman he had loved as mother, *was* his mother. Iesous, Little Star, was Little Star's blood brother. And, through Iesous, Echon was his blood brother, too. One did not spill a brother's blood. It would be very hard to explain all this to Tonneraouanont who was also his and Iesous' brother. But he would try. Maybe he would succeed. Had not Tonneraouanont said he might one day be *oki?*

There was loss as well as gain, though. There was always loss as well as gain. It was the law of life. Somewhat sadly Little Star realized that he could never be *oki* now. Only *orenda.* But *orenda* was much. The friends of the Great Spirit were *orenda.* That he had always known. Now he knew a new and good thing. The Great Spirit, who was Father, and the Little Spirit, His Son, were *oki.* So was that Spirit who, as Echon said, proceeded from them both. Here, lying in the birchen cradle, was an image of the only true *oki.* No man could become *oki.* But *oki* had become man. It was enough, and more than enough. The white men, who were the red men's brothers, called these ancient forests of the Huron a New World. Now, for the people of the Bear as well, who from of old had known these dark trees and lakes, it was truly a new world, too, at last. At last, and for the first time. Even if the wars he saw in Tonneraouanont's magic fire had to come — and Little Star thought they so had to come — even if the animals, his other brothers, had to die — and Little Star feared they so had to die — it was a new world and a good one. And it was the gift of Iesous, his brother. What could Little Star give this little Day Star in return?

Little Star thought he knew. Among the other gifts at the crib he would place his arrowhead of sacred flint. It would be a good toy for the Child. He would keep the bow, though. It was a good bow for hunting his brother, the deer. In moons to come there would be time enough to learn more about these good tidings Echon brought across the Ocean water to the Bear people. Meanwhile, tomorrow he would sing a life song for the Little Star. Tomorrow on his lodge pennon he would paint a Child and a Star. But *N-an-gohs* would never be *Che-na-n-goh* now. The Great Spirit had not spurned becoming the Little Spirit. Little Star would stay Little Star in homage to Him who had come from the East to be the Little Star of the Hurons.

It was cold inside the bark house after the bright blinding beauty of the service in which Echon had drunk the Great Spirit's blood out of his golden cup. That was a hard saying Little Star was hard put to make anything of. But he meant to learn. Forward in time the child, who, too, was orenda, stirred on her couch before Louis Bourdon's fire. But she did not wake yet. There was more to come. N-an-gohs had receded now, and Moira was returning. Returning, not yet returned. She would not remember when she woke. But she would know.

It was dark inside the bark house after the candles were snuffed — all but one to write by. In the chilling room the smell of the stale incense was like grit in the mouth. No fire burned except for a small brazier of charcoal to keep the ink from freezing. Wearily the great priest, whom the people of the Bear called Echon, raised his massive head from the log-hewn table onto which, for a moment or two, it had sunk. In a fine sloping hand he wrote the final lines of his letter to the Reverend Father Paul Le Jeune, Superior of the Mission of the Society of Jesus in New France, presently resident in Quebec:

> *I love my red brothers in Christ as well as I have loved any man. But sometimes I despair of teaching them the sweet evangel of the Child. The evil is they are so attached to their old customs that, knowing the beauty of truth, they are content to approve it without embracing it. Their usual reply is: oniondechouten. That is: Such is the custom of our country.*
>
> *I am afraid there is little we can do to fight this argument. Certainly we have not here that exterior solemnity which awakens and sustains devotion — any more, I console myself by remembering, than had the Magi long ago in the stable.*
>
> *Written at the Residence of Saint Joseph in the Huron Country, at the Village called Ihonatiria, this twenty-fifth morning of December, 1636.*
>
> > *Your very humble and obedient servant in our Lord,*
> > *Jean de Brébeuf*

Outside, in the darkness that is just before dawn, while the Evening Star — not yet the Morning Star — still burned bright over Echon's ridge pole, the animals came adoring, in their noiseless ranks, the little Lord of birds and beasts. Silent they stood in the black velvet shadow of the pines. The wild creatures who were to die: ptarmigan, deer, squirrel, turkey, puma, beaver, mink, raccoon, porcupine. They were led in their quiet files by the four living creatures whom another star-gazer, not unlike the Huron boy, *N-an-gohs*, one named Ezekiel, had seen long centuries before on the hills of Palestine. Tireless, voiceless, huge, majestic they stood, the archangelic archetypes of the totems: great eagle, great lion, great buffalo, ringing, against the coming of the Serpent, the house where this night lay the Babe. The manshape, tall *Iouskeha*, was there. *Iouskeha*, giver of corn, keeper of the animals. So, too, was the Great Bear of the Hurons, who were the people of the Bear.

As the darkness withdrew before the coming of the light, it began to snow again. Still the great beasts stood there, dumb and patient. Snow mailed the eagle feathers. It whitened the buffalo muzzle and blanched the dark lion mane. It silvered the dark pelt of the Great Bear of the Hurons. By morning all Ihonatiria was covered with the soft-shafted flakes. Snow fell all through that day and the next, arrowing across gray light and whitened dark, muffling the bark huts up to their smoke-holes. Nothing could be seen of Little Star's ridge pole but the painted Child and the Star he had set upon his lodge pennon.

A gray dawn broke over Louis Bourdon's cabin. Ihonatiria, city of the Hurons, was only a point in time again. Over Christian Island the air was white with falling snow.

"Wake up, Moira," said Professor Desmond, gently shaking her by the shoulder. There was a silvery light in the room: early morning and snow together. The fire burned brightly. Marie set bacon and eggs before the child. Louis was buckling their bags together. The old lady watched her solemnly from beside the fireplace. When Moira said good-by, the old lady bowed and said the strange words over and over again.

"*Orenda, orenda,*" she said. "*Orenda, N-an-gohs.*"

Marie kissed her as she stood on the doorstep.

"Good-by, Little Star," she said, slipping a package into her coat pocket. "Take this in memory of our meeting. But do not open it till you get home."

Outside there were tracks on the snow. Big tracks. Professor Desmond raised his eyebrows.

"Bear," said Louis Bourdon, looking at his wife. "Big bear. I have never trapped so big a bear."

With one mittened hand Louis Bourdon clapped the child on the shoulder.

"Your bear, Little Star," he said.

And he did not smile.

"Hmm," said Professor Desmond, measuring the pads with his eye. "If we were further north, I should say that was a Kodiak track."

"No Kodiak," said Louis Bourdon. "Bigger than Kodiak. The Great Bear."

Professor Desmond found himself suddenly reluctant to argue the point. He shrugged his shoulders.

Joe Bourdon's boat loomed up spectral through a drifting curtain of snow.

"Hurry," Joe urged them. "Big snow coming."

The snow was already six inches thick around their car wheels, when they climbed ashore at Honey Harbor. Professor Desmond gunned the motor into life. Joe transferred the bags again from the launch to the rear trunk. Moira looked across the water into a strange world of whiteness and nothing else.

"Drive steady, but not too fast," said Joe, when they were ready to push off. "You will ride it out."

Joe was right. Even taking out three quarters of an hour for Mass at Orillia, they advanced faster than the storm. Fifty miles north of Toronto, the roads were bare again. Professor Desmond tuned in to the weather report. The snow was already a foot and a half deep in Georgian Bay, and beginning to drift. The same was true of the Muskokas. By evening it would sweep down into southern Ontario and the Niagara region. But their luck held, and by evening they were safe and warm in Buffalo.

Before she sank to sleep in her own bed, Moira opened Marie Bourdon's little package. It contained a beautifully cured deerskin pouch tied with a drawstring. Inside was an arrowhead of flint, its edges lined with blue, marked with a cross on either surface; and a smooth-rubbed moonstone on a deer thong. Moira put these new treasures on her knickknack shelf next to her miniature Notre Dame football. Sheila's shelf alongside had a Dresden figurine with fili-greed China dress, and a Carmen Miranda doll complete with ear-rings. Carmen Miranda stood on a music box. When you turned her, the box played *Song of the Swamp*. The doll tinkled a little now as Moira set down arrowhead and moonstone on the next shelf.

Before Professor Desmond went to bed, he looked in on Kristin. She and Bozo were sleeping in one bed. They both were still wearing cowboy hats and gun holsters. The first flakes of snow were just whispering at the nursery window, and the wind was rising, as he switched off the light again.

With a smile Professor Desmond improved on Goethe.

"*Wer reitet so spät*," he intoned to himself, "*durch Nacht und Wind?*

Es ist die Kristie mit Bozo Kind."

Yes, he said to himself, yawning, Childe Bozo is quite a character. Of the lineage of the Bear's Son on the bar sinister side. It had been a good trip. The Christian Island analogue just about clinched the evidence of the Tuscarora tale. Somehow, somewhere, an old Viking story had gotten loose among the Indians of New York and Ontario. And, so far as he could date it, it seemed to confirm the hypothesis of early Viking penetration into the interior of the American continent. Now there, said Professor Desmond, dropping one shoe in his excitement, was a subject fit for a prince of story-tellers. Leif, son of Eric, was a much greater hero than the Son of the Bear, whoever that ursine gentleman might have been. And Leif marched out of the Gate of Horn, not out of the Gate of Ivory whence came riding the false dreams at nightfall. If dreams were ever false, that was. Or ever true.

On the other side of the wall Moira turned in her sleep and said something. Professor Desmond looked in on her again. Damp ringlets framed her face. She moved and spoke once more. Blowing a last kiss and shutting the door, Professor Desmond wondered out of which gate rode her present dream.

The colonial clock chimed twelve in the darkness of downstairs.

CHAPTER FOUR

Christmas in Buffalo

BEFORE Professor Desmond set out for his last class before the
Christmas recess, Kristin hugged him as usual. Then they played
their customary game of *Owl* which involved rubbing noses together, eyes closed, and quickly opening their eyes again at this
close range.

Kristin squealed in delight.

"You've got two little televisions in your eyes," she said to her
father.

"By George!" said Professor Desmond, admiringly. "That's not
bad. Did you hear what the kid says, Toby? She says I've got two
little television sets in my eyes."

"Kids are baby goats! Kids are baby goats!" Kristin chanted, dancing about him.

Professor Desmond bowed to her formally, hat held against his
chest.

"Forgive my use of the vernacular," he said, picking up his briefcase.

That little *entr'acte* had been at four o'clock in the afternoon.
Now, at eight in the evening with only a half hour to go to the
end of his *Béowulf* seminar, Professor Desmond wished he had two
little televisions in his classroom as well as in his eyes. At the
moment, the televisions in his eyes did not seem hypnotic enough
for the purpose in hand. The undergraduate glee club was caroling
in the quad outside his window. In the girls' lounge some student

nurses appeared to be swinging a boogie-woogie *Silent Night*. The Dramatic Club was presenting some sort of bucolic hoe-down in their club rooms directly below him. And he — God save the mark! — was holding forth, like some latter-day Scrooge, on the metaphysics of the Anglo-Saxon idea of fate.

The operative Old English texts and their translations were neatly printed on the blackboard. In green and red chalk in honor of the season.

Gæð a wyrd swa hio scel!
Fate works out ever as it wills.

Wyrd oft nereð unfægne eorl, ðonne his ellen deah.
Fate often spares the unfated jarl whose courage is good.

Ac him Dryhten forgeaf wigspeda gewiofu.
But the Lord granted him good fate in war.

"Notice," said Professor Desmond, clearing this throat and rapping with a pointer on the blackboard. "By the eighth century of the Christian era, the Teutonic idea of fate was no longer that of an utterly immutable force. Our first quotation would suggest that it was, of course. *Fate works out ever as it wills.* But just look at the second: *Fate often spares the unfated jarl whose courage is good.* A sort of combination, you see, of *God helps those who help themselves* and *Pray to God, and keep your powder dry.* We seem to be on our way to that popular song of World War II: *Praise the Lord and Pass the Ammunition.*"

Professor Desmond's mind had begun to wander. Then he came to himself with a start.

"Wyrd," he said. "Wyrd. Yes. Notice the etymological derivation of the idea. Fate, to the Anglo-Saxons, was *wyrd*: that which becomes. Not at all unlike, you see, the nineteenth-century German transcendental notion of *Werden*, reality always becoming. One can tell a lot about a national psyche from the different national words for fate. To the Roman fate was *fatum*: that which is uttered. Even as to the Moslems it is still *Kismet*: that which is allotted. Ideas, you will note, that imply an utterer and an allotter. Christians allow for the concept of *providence*: divine wisdom foreseeing and divine charity forestalling. You may, for example, recall here *Ham-*

let's: We defy augury. There is a special providence in the fall of a sparrow. An advance, is it not, over what we find in *Oedipus Rex* — Sophocles' haunting theorem of the intersection of fate and free will on the plane of time? And yet related, too. As if the pagans thought of fate as an impersonal providence, and the Christians of providence as a personal fate. Greek tragedy nobly reconciled man with fate — *la condition humaine,* as it were. The Christian fairy tale, on its highest as well as lowest levels — Mozart's music, the fairy scherzo of Shakespeare's *Tempest,* as well as the folk stenography of the Brothers Grimm — reconciles man with the paradisal promise that was in the beginning: *la condition surhumaine.* Who is to say which is the higher art? It is easy to say which is the more consoling idea."

Someone coughed in the rear of the classroom. Professor Desmond came to himself again with another spasmodic jerk. The clock registered eight twenty-seven. It was high time to begin his peroration.

"The elder gods dwindle," he said. "Kronos devours his children — all but one, his little step-son in the crib whose beast-thronged cave dethroned god-thronged Olympus. Remember Yeats' great line on Bethlehem? *The uncontrollable mystery of the bestial floor?* Yes, the mystery remains uncontrollable even two thousand years after. The elder gods dwindle into Christmas goblins and household brownies. *Wyrd* declines into *weird.* But even *weird* has power still. For a diminished fate remains uncanny. Shakespeare's three weird sisters are the Norns, the Fates, the three spinning — er, wenches."

Why had he faltered over "wenches"? It was because his first impulse had been to say "bitches," and he was really too old-fashioned for such Hemingwayisms in the classroom. That was what a dear friend of his, who had died in the Huertgen Forest, used to call the Fates: the three spinning bitches, Clothos, Athos, and Porthos. It was really Clotho, Lachesis, and Atropos, of course. His old friend had been longer on Dumas than on Greek mythology.

Another cough — this time from the front of the classroom. The clock now marked eight twenty-nine. He must get on.

"*Fatum* dwindled, too," he said. "Into *fée* first. Then into *fay.* Then into *fairy.* Because of the conquest of the Child, the ancient master of gods and men, old Destiny, is now no more than a Sugar

Plum fairy atop a Christmas tree. . . . Ladies and gentlemen, I wish you a holy, a happy, and a most convivial Christmas."

While he gathered up his papers, Professor Desmond somewhat embarrassedly wondered why an old campaigner like himself had closed on this holy note. Unless one was a clergyman, that is, a professional, words like "holy" had a ring of cant about them. He did not feel particularly canting now, though, as he walked briskly into the cool night out to his car.

Over the quadrangle the Chapel carillon pealed out the three quarters. The Chapel door was open. Students were carrying spruce and fir boughs in for the Christmas decorations. One could see the red sanctuary lamp winking before the altar. Professor Desmond cocked an experienced eye at the sky. One quickly grew weatherwise in Buffalo. It looked like a snow sky, if he was any judge. The air began to have a raw edge to it. The middle reaches of the heavens were still clear, but on the horizon line huge snow clouds were massing. Like himself, the clouds had apparently been woolgathering. Their fleece hung heavy on the night. Three of them — gray sister clouds humped over spindles of air — were moving up over the Chapel where now, at the end of Advent, lay the little Lord of the Norns waiting patiently for the Feast of His Nativity.

As it happened, Professor Desmond had forgotten to comment on the best text of all. *Ac him Dryhten forgeaf wigspeda gewiofu. But the Lord granted him good fate in war.* There was, for one thing, the metaphor involved in *gewiofu.* It meant, literally, *weaving.* He could have done wonders with the concept of warp and woof in destiny. And now it was too late. The college janitor, a brown stub of cigarette dangling from the corner of his mouth, and whistling *Adeste Fideles*, was sponging the text forever from the board.

If it was too late for further classroom exposition, it was never too late on the chronometer of destiny. At this precise point in time the great dicing presences, who weave by lot the warp and woof of history, cast their ivory die again. The pattern they presently wove was subtler than, say, that of an afghan rug or a patchwork quilt some mother of a family might work over on a long winter evening such as this one. Like the circus bedspread, for example, Mrs. Desmond was even now hurrying to finish for Kristin's Christmas morning. Theirs was a pattern stiff with heraldic figures like the figures of the Bayeux Tapestry. One could make out already an American eagle and a Soviet sickle; a British lion and a French cock; and something — this, though, was not extra clear — that, when finished, might bear some resemblance to the old imperial bird of the Hohenzollerns. There was one corner square still empty except for the outline of a dragon ship under sail. It would very much surprise the Desmond family to know that their name was being woven into that same oblong by the impersonal, flying fingers of the Fates, forever busy blocking out the shape of the ultimate, the unattainable republic.

The twentieth was an amazing century in more ways than one. Perhaps the most amazing thing about it was the way in which old fate had managed to get itself writ large again as the new Science, the new Religion, the new Politics, according to the noncommittal creeds of biological, sociological, historic determinism. Life was no longer a lottery for the elect. It was a sure thing. A single choice early in the game, and one was safe forever. No need — in fact, no chance — to choose again. The little man who stood just outside the lamp post's pool of light, smoking a cigarette and patiently watching the front entrance of 2121 Massachusetts Avenue, Washington, D. C., had chosen very early in the game indeed. The luminous dial face of his wrist watch marked eight forty-five in the evening.

The name on the little man's driver's license read Dirk Tietjens. That was not his name, of course. A short time ago the license in the leather wallet had borne the name Saul Tikjan; and that was not his real name, either. At least, it was not the name his parents had given him at birth. But it was closer than Tietjens at that; and, like Tietjens, it preserved a kind of psychic nexus with the long Armenian name another kind of fate had allotted him over forty-three years ago somewhere in the teeming Levant. His names, be it noted, had nothing to do with the case. They might as well have been Jones or Smith or Robinson or Kelly. What had made him a docile neophyte of destiny was a certain definite act of

spiritual volition consummated in time and space, not any accident
of blood or birth or creed. He had freely willed to slay freedom.
This one thing, at least, was not determined for him.

The little man's face was narrow, and pointed at nose and chin.
It would be commonplace, but true, to say he looked like a rat.
One of the newer painters would probably have painted him with
a green skin which, again, would have been inexact, but perhaps
not too impossibly inexact. He had few assets for the indifferent
society into which he had been born; and fewer still for the hospitable
society which, in an excess of both hope and despair, he had
temporarily chosen at the end of the Twenties, and to which he
still maintained a sort of nominal, strategic allegiance. Among those
assets were patience, accuracy, and an infinite capacity for never
being bored. The sinister society, which now employed him both
as tool and votary, knew how to exploit those assets.

The little man with the *crème de menthe* complexion did not
anticipate a very long vigil. His present quarry, whose habits he now
knew as intimately as he did his own, was much too methodical
for that. This, undoubtedly, was the result of his quarry's German
background; and that, when one analyzed it, was still another variety
of fate. At precisely nine o'clock this quarry of his would come out
of the *Cosmos Club*, turn to the right, and walk to Sheridan Circle
where a green-bronze statue of the Civil War cavalry general cur-
vetted, rampant, into the dripping December sky. He would walk
around the circle, stand, leaning back against a cane, for something
like five minutes — never more and rarely less — post a letter or two
in the mail box, and return to the *Cosmos Club*.

It was an old Washington joke that the *Cosmos Club* represented
brains and no money, the *Metropolitan Club* money and no brains,
and the *Army and Navy Club* neither brains nor money. If, as jests
had a habit of being, this one was true, then Dr. Gottfried Krehan,
whilom Professor of Physics, political specialist for the last Bruening
government, close friend of Konrad Adenauer, was well qualified
for his present residency therein. He had no money whatsoever,
plenty of brains, and tremendous personal integrity. He was, in
addition, a German patriot in the good sense of that much abused
word, and an expert in German electoral law. With important West
German elections expected in the near future, in both of these

latter capacities Dr. Krehan was a source of considerable interest, and even some anxiety, to Mr. Tietjens' unidentified and unidentifiable employers in the Washington *apparat* of the Communist Party.

Dr. Krehan did not alter his meticulous schedule by a single minute this twenty-second night of December. At precisely nine o'clock he came out of the *Cosmos Club*, turned right to Sheridan Circle, smoked his cigar and contemplated the equestrian statue that was filmed over tonight with a fat skin of wet fog.

As he smoked, Dr. Krehan thought on many things: of his student days in the Russia that used to be; of his reading Pushkin and Lermontov and Gogol and Dostoevski; of the many masks the peoples of the world wore before the vain mirror of history. Leaning on his stick, he thought for some few moments on that great and terrifying symbol in Gogol of Mother Russia as a fairy-tale troika rushing irresistibly through the snowy night of history, while all other peoples and nations, standing aside, gave it the right of way. He thought also of Prosecutor Kirillovich's famous epigram in *The Brothers Karamazov*: *No, gentlemen of the jury, they have their Hamlets, but we still have our Karamazovs.* Was it still true of Russia, that she had those God-drunk souls, the Karamazovs? As for the Western world, it still had its indecisive Hamlets, all right. It also had — a factor Dostoevski had been too early in time to measure — its Huckleberry Finns.

And its Galahads. An American Army Major walked through the misty night, past Dr. Krehan and General Sheridan. Erect as only a West Pointer can be erect. Immaculate as a young god. And innocent. The English had had this kind of military innocence in the century that was past. It had passed now to the Americans. The continental peoples had never had it, least of all those seasoned militarists, his countrymen. Dr. Krehan sighed and resumed his walk.

Another mask of Muscovy — one of the latest ones — watched him. It was expressionless, anonymous, emptied of personality. When Dr. Krehan turned again into the *Cosmos Club*, the mask came alive. Coolly, efficiently, working with wire tongs and calipers, it abstracted the mail from the post box. Those letters that, in their upper left hand corner, bore Dr. Krehan's precisely written return address were slipped into a coat pocket, to be steamed open later, read, a note made of their contents, resealed, and remailed. One of Krehan's missives was a Christmas card, sent off with true professorial frugality without benefit of envelope. Mr. Tietjens took down the address in a flexible leather book he kept for that purpose:

Professor and Mrs. John C. Desmond,
731 Hurst Monceux,
Kenmore Post Office,
Buffalo 23,
N. Y.

The card, a German-made one in charming pastels, carried a picture of a Christ Child holding a Christmas tree, left hand raised in benediction over a snowy city. Printed on it in Gothic characters was the inscription: *Alle Jahre Wieder Kommt Das Christuskind.* It was signed: *Gottfried.* Mr. Tietjens took it in the gloved finger tips of his right hand, and dropped it back in the mailbox. It lay there, quiet, cheek by jowl with the usual week-before-Christmas quota of English coaches, holly wreaths, poinsettias, paper martinis waggishly inscribed, and sophisticated cherubs four centuries after Raphael and just as theologically improper as the Divine Painter's own spoon-faced seraphs.

Professor Desmond had been right about the snow. It set in around midnight of the twenty-third, just two days after fall, according to calendar time, had officially withdrawn and winter officially come in.

The midnight flakes fell lazy over Canada. The red gods of the Senecas heard them first as, thirty miles from the city line, the flakes whispered, insistent in the whitening night, against the Long House mossed and silvered council logs. They drifted about the Tuscarora cabins. The Peace Bridge stood quiet in the falling flakes: ghost plinth and spectre span. In Forest Lawn a granite kepi whitened. White peace of snow invested the freezing Iliad of metal warrior on Lafayette Square across from the blurring red brick keep, the Gothic donjon of the old Library. Professor Desmond moved in his sleep, dreaming of the snow that fell years back on Huertgen Forest. Into Moira's dream came felt-shod caribou and elk. How was it with Korea? With Gettysburg's dark glades?

With Valley Forge? With Ardennes woods and Argonne cemetery?

Bell towers rose into the argent hush. They matched their chimes against the white berceuse that mantled, softened, silvered, but did not still them utterly. Hayes Hall's clock carillon; State College's leash of bells cast loose athwart the pacing steeds of night and snow. St. Paul's dove-cote of sound, clear pigeon flutter of music. Wesminster's campanile. St. Michael's Jesuit bronze. The hoarse throat of that iron Kenmore bell which still swung over the little chapel where, one hundred years before, John Nepomucene Neumann, priest of Prague, had blessed the white bread of God for dark Indian faces. Oziel Smith, stanch North Bush Protestant, gave him that chapel site in token that, in Christ, all men were brothers.

From the upper windows of a darkened downtown building — Dickens might have drawn, Melville painted, those Quaker rooms, but not those monstrous presses — the night watchman for the *Buffalo Evening News* looked out over a lake that was beginning to be wrapped now in a winding sheet of whited air. He could not see those stream-lined predators of summer and winter skies alike, the Viking gulls. But he could almost feel their freezing feathers on his back. Mewing, they circled the dark water — it had not frozen over yet — circled the long ships docked till returning spring should unlock their cold harbor. On the Canadian shore, the little houses were already lost to sight in the driving snow.

Steadily the long white swales piled up about the Zoo, mounding the storm fences, pearling the dawn light under which the animals slept. Only the camels, prescient, woke, remembering . . .

The kitchen was full of a pleasant baking smell when Professor Desmond came downstairs, freshly shaven, on the morning of the twenty-fourth. Norwegian cookies. *Julekakke.* Santa Clauses cut out with cookie cutters and lightly dusted with colored sugar. Mother was humming some plaintive bars of *Solveig's Song* from *Peer Gynt*.

"Aha, Toby!" said Professor Desmond, quoting as usual. "*A sad tale's best for winter. There was a man dwelt by a church yard.*"

After breakfast Professor Desmond got down to work. The tree had to be brought in from the garage and set in its standard. The light sets had to be tested. The tree ornaments had to be carried down from the unheated attic. Ditto the snow man family, the assorted crèches, the Nuremberg Madonna angel who held two candles stiffly in her hands, the miniature Santa Clauses — all twelve of them — the wooden Nisse carrying the lantern, the little Norwegian tree with the toy wheat sheaves on it, the dancing paper goblins, the *Julebukken* with the dwarf on its back.

Red-cheeked, her plaid snow-suit sparkling with fresh-fallen snow crystals, Karen came in, just as her father finished arranging the greens and holly about the base of the Viking ship on the mantel. The ship was a delicately made scale model in green bronze of the Oseberg queen's barge. It stood on an ornamental base, which was inscribed:

Oseberg Skipet
Norsk Viking
Langskip — Tiende Aarhundrede

This meant, quite simply: "Oseberg Ship. Norse Viking Longship. Tenth Century." It was Toby's bride-present from her husband, and the Desmond family's most prized possession.

"I've something to show you, Dad," Karen said shyly. "It's in the playroom."

"One minute," he said, his hands full of wooden angels now, "till I finish setting up this celestial fish fry in the whatnot."

It seemed to Professor Desmond that, in or out of the Christmas season, the living room was overstocked both with angels and with small busts of Beethoven and Mozart. The angels were tolerable, he supposed. At least they were variegated. Angels on skis. Angels playing on timbrels. Jim Crow angels. Angels *ad infinitum*, which was a much more theological way of putting it than to say *ad nauseam*. The composers' busts, though, were unqualifiedly *ad nauseam*. Three identical little Beethovens. Three identical little Mozarts.

"Can't we do something about this surplus population of *Kapellmeistern?*" he said plaintively to Karen. "For example, how about removing these two?"

"Those are mine," said Karen. "I got them for playing the *Andante* in Beethoven's *Fifth Symphony*."

"Oh," said Professor Desmond. "How about getting rid of these, then?" He pointed to another little Beethoven and another little Mozart on the grand piano.

"Those are Moira's," said Karen. "She got them for playing Papageno's *Magic Melody* — I think it's from *The Magic Flute*."

"I wish I had a *Zauberflöte* myself," said Professor Desmond. "I suppose Sheila got this third pair for playing the *Barrel House Boogie*."

"No," said Karen, laughing. "Her recital piece was *In a Rose Garden*."

"I bet she played it in boogie-woogie," said Professor Desmond. "Everything she plays comes out boogie-woogie."

"There's something in the playroom I want you to see," said Karen.

"Oh, yes," said Professor Desmond. "Sorry. I'll come along at once."

The "something" in the playroom was the end of an era. Karen had, without warning, swept the board clean of childhood's bric-a-brac. Fourteen years lay neatly stacked in a clothes basket: the prized treasures of yesterday. There were her lead soldiers. Eight knights in silver gilt mail, the red paint not yet rubbed off their lances. Eight charging Zulus with spears and assegais. Eight Indian chiefs in full war panoply. There were her metal dinosaurs from the Museum Story Hour. There was her Russian doll, and her two Polish ones. A lump came into Professor Desmond's throat. He was utterly unprepared for the child's sweeping démarche. This was the first of fatherhood's great divides. And he was not ready. Parents were never ready. It was like a little death.

"I kept the rubber animals," she said.

It fitted. He could almost have predicted that. The animals were "chichi" enough for the eyes of the gang. Professor Desmond felt a sudden pang of pity for his red-haired daughter. Youth was so terribly vulnerable. No longer child, not woman yet, she crossed the no-man's, no-woman's land of life now. Conformity began — on the outside. In evening bags and stockings and lipsticks and corsages. Inside, to compensate, she would be more fiercely individualistic than ever. The metaphysics of wonder shifted to another plane. Gone the easy magic of the fairy who lived in the olive, of the tooth under the pillow and the gleaming dime in the morning; of the wooden Pinocchio on the desk, of the leprechaun's gold. Now began the Year of the Boy, of the lion male. From now on, however demure she seemed, it would be Karen, huntress. Until the good time came for her to be Karen, mother.

"I thought you might want to keep the knights and the dinosaurs," she said. "The girls can have the other things."

The child was very sensitive. He felt moved again — absurdly so. This would be a woman of gentilesse and courtoisie — only the old words would do here.

"Thank you, dear," said Professor Desmond. "I should like to have them very much. . . . And now I have something for you."

He undid a little box, and handed her the sprig of mistletoe within. The spray was pale green and cold to touch; and the silver gray berries were clouded over as if wood sprites had just breathed upon them. Truly the mistletoe was a plant of power. For him, at least, it was the silver bough that called up all the dark oak forest where it first quickened into magic life.

Karen kissed him gaily.

"Is this a hint, Dad?" she asked.

He kissed her back.

"Say a symbol," he said. "And a spell. And beware. It is a dangerous spell. It killed a god once. The bright god, Baldr."

Who was Baldr? Riddle him that! Professor Desmond was glad the child had not asked him that question. Baldr was innocence as well as wisdom. Baldr was light. Baldr was love. How could love slay love?

Professor Desmond looked down at his watch. Baldr was also Norse; and it was time for him to pick up the Norsemen in his family. Or, to be exact, the Norseman. Grandmother Hansen was *ante-bellum* Washington, of Scotch-Irish stock and Confederate sympathy. She didn't have too much truck with all this Norse business that seemed to enrapture the rest of the family. Professor Desmond was not really sure that Grandmother Hansen had ever accepted the verdict of either Appomattox or of her own marriage ceremony with its archaic demands about obedience on the part of wives.

But Grandfather Hansen was a Norseman all right. He was an apple-cheeked little man who, at seventy-five, still could pass for fifty, even as, at fifty, he had already looked middle-aged. Professor Desmond had an inveterate habit — his wife called it a bad habit — of casting people for a fancy dress ball. He had never made up his mind whether Grandfather Hansen should come as a naval officer in white drill, as Pickwick in a blue coat with gold buttons, or as the jolly old man in Hans Andersen who sat under the Christmas tree and told the children the story of Avede Avede, and the tale of Trille Lille, the Scandinavian Humpty Dumpty. Grandfather Hansen's bedroom, in his apartment, was like a toy shop. In it he had a wooden model of the Gokstad Viking ship, and a super shadow box with Napoleon and his marshals standing at salute against a charcoal and pastel chalk background of the Champ de Mars.

Grandfather Hansen's mind was crisscrossed not only with the tracks of Napoleon's greater campaigns, but with the fine print of time tables and railroad schedules. He went each Sunday to a Lutheran church of the Missouri Synod where the services were still conducted in Norwegian. It was one of Professor Desmond's pleasanter Christmas chores to take him there and wait for him Christmas morning. He liked his father-in-law passing well, and thanked his lucky stars that he was so easy to get along with.

In one way, perhaps he was too easy to get along with. It exasperated Grandmother Hansen that Grandfather could not be goaded into argument with her. It exasperated her, and it left her more energy to argue with others. Grandmother Hansen dearly loved an argument. It was her spirited substitute for bridge and canasta. One would suspect that she inherited this litigious tendency from her Southern family, who all lived at an operatic pitch, at the tops of their voices, as it were, never wrote when they could telephone, regulated their social relationships according to the code duello, and were, like Grandmother Hansen herself, as lovable as they were inconsistent.

Mother had the Christmas Eve smörgäsbord all ready on the table when Professor Desmond got back with Grandmother and Grandfather Hansen. There was pickled herring for Grandfather, tytebær for the children, and gjetost for Mother. There was also a whipped-cream syllabub for the red-capped Nisse who lived in the

fireplace. This was called *fløtdagrøt*. When no one was looking,
Rajah and Ranee, both of whom had sweet tooths, lapped up the
Nisse's custard. Sillerton Jackson stuck to herring.

"We've a surprise for you, *Bestefar*," said Professor Desmond
after the candles were lighted and they had all sat down at table.
"Kristin will say grace tonight."

And, in a quite tolerable Norwegian accent, Kristin proceeded to
recite:

> *"I Jesu navn går vi til bord,*
> *A spise, drikke, på dit ord.*
> *Dig, Gud, til ære og oss til gavn,*
> *Så får vi mat i Jesu navn."*

Which, Englished, went something like this:

> *In Jesus's name go we to the board,*
> *To eat, to drink, in Jesus' word.*
> *Through God the Father Jesus came,*
> *So we sip and we sup in Jesus' name.*

It was the high point of the Christmas season for *Bestefar* Hansen.
He sat there at the head of his daughter's table, beaming, smiling,
nodding his head, saying nothing, back in the little whaling town
of his childhood where, in the long, long ago, he, too, had once
been the youngest in the family, and so had been entrusted with
the important duty of reciting the quaint old Lutheran grace.

"The child has a good accent, John," said Grandmother Hansen,
approvingly.

After supper, Professor Desmond drew the flowered mohair drapes
across the living room windows, and switched on the tree. Then
they opened the out-of-town presents, which, since they came by
post in open daylight, were considered outside Santa's jurisdiction.
After the presents, the family looked at the cards stacked in the
card container. Professor Desmond held up one card with a Christ
Child on it.

"From Gottfried Krehan," he said. "With a Washington post-
mark. So he's in this country."

When the children were all in bed — including that great child,
Grandfather Hansen who kept farmers' hours — Mother and Grandmother Hansen filled the stockings in the kitchen. Professor Des-

mond went over to the living room windows, drew back the drapes again, and looked out. It was still snowing, but more quietly now. The tree lights laid soft scarves of deep blue, and green, and red, across the snow-mantled evergreens. He picked a copy of *Pickwick* off one of the fireplace's flanking bookshelves, and opened to the Dingley Dell chapters. Ah, there was the passage he wanted. The very essence of a snowy Christmas in two short lines.

> *"How it snows!" said one of the men, in a low tone.*
> *"Snows, does it?" said Wardle.*

Yes, he said to himself, the popular instinct was right in demanding a white Christmas. If only on its cards. The great Christmas mood was contrast, a counterpoint of snow and fire. Of wind howling outside, and inside old Fezziwig rosily dancing. Even as the great Christmas theme was reversal. The forest came into the houses of men. According to the topsy-turvy protocol of Bethlehem — a bedlam protocol, if there ever was one — shepherds preceded kings. And animals preceded shepherds. Poor clerks were exalted and rich misers humbled.

The final few hours of Christmas Eve excitement exacted their toll at last. Yawning a little, Professor Desmond poured himself a glass of holiday port. Outside, in the winter night, the snow had yielded to a mighty cold. Bleak with chill, the tree trunks creaked. Branches snapped. From Lackawanna all the way to Niagara Falls, along lake and river and gorge, church spires pricked into a sky ablaze with stars. Cold pearled the bubble-blown dome of the Jesuit College on Main Street, and the onion-bulbed domes of the Greek churches near the Steel Plant. Frost rime silvered the angels' trumpets upraised atop the Basilica of Our Lady of Victory. The stained glass of Trinity Lutheran was rimed outside with silver. On Delaware Park's white altar cloth of meadow snow, one lone celebrant oak lifted up a winter wafer moon. Downtown, nothing moved except the wind. A perfect icicle in stone, the obelisk of McKinley Monument, pointed, like some great moon dial, into the jeweled movement of the stars. The Great Bear glittered, lonely. Orion bent his cold bright bow of stars at the strange star called Earth.

Merry Christmas! May the Mass of Christ be merry! On his way to Midnight Mass, the clear night air was wine in Professor Desmond's nostrils, and the greenwood gums ot spruce and balsam stayed sticky on his palms. He bore the forests on his hands; and that, too, was part of the Christmas essence. Part of the magic, the wonder. The forest had contracted into a single tree. Christmas celebrated the miniature — what Grandfather Hansen liked, caressingly, to call *småting*. Small things. Christmas was divinity become small. Christmas was the cosmos viewed through the wrong end — tonight, though, it was the right end — of some toy telescope of love and innocence, till the court of heaven dwindled into a tiny *crèche*, till archangels shrank into table decorations. Even — God save the mark! — into Calder *mobiles*. When all was said and done, Professor Desmond thought he liked Calder *mobiles*. As far as angels went, a Calder *mobile* was much closer to the wheels-with-eyes of Revelation than was either Raphael or Bertha Hummel.

And another thing. As God became small at Christmastide, so did man become large through God's largesse. If God had become man, so had man become God. Simultaneously, as the forest diminished to a single tree, so did the living room spread out into the northern woods. Fireplaces expanded into the pulsing heart of the world. A gilt star grew more important than the sun. The Son was *Sol Invictus*. And the Son became man.

The lighted houses along his way, with their spun sugar windows opening on the snow, seemed pure Humperdinck to Professor Desmond. Almost good enough to eat. The great quadrangle of land on Englewood Avenue, occupied by church, school, convent, chapel, and priest's house, was a Christmas card, banal and beautiful. Professor Desmond was glad the old pastor had stuck to his guns in insisting on a kind of Congregationalist architecture for his new buildings, against the irritated protests of the parishioners who were conditioned to nothing but Romanesque, Gothic, and Italian marble. Until the Church should evolve a new style suited to the American ethos, let her assimilate the sort of architecture that, over the centuries, had nestled into the American landscape and into the American heart.

The doors of the little chapel were open, as well as those of the new church. The little chapel had been the site of an Indian mission many years before in the generation after the burning of Buffalo by British troops, when the memory of Red Jacket, the great orator of the Senecas, was still green in the land. The choirs were practicing. Sweet strains of *Adeste Fideles*, the sweeter for being muted by distance, drifted out across the snow.

After the midnight service began, so great was the press of people that, despite the coldness of the night, the ushers left the doors open. This was the beginning, this Mass before dawn. Soon, in the early morning hours, all Buffalo would go to worship, Grandfather Hansen among them.

The singing faded down wind into the night, into the cold, into the Indian forests of the past, where, three hundred years before this holy night, Huron throats had raised the deathless chant:

> *Ouarie onnaouakoueton ndio sen tsatonnharonnion*
> *Iesous ahatonnia!*
> So the angels tell their glad Gospel:
> Mary has borne the Great Spirit!
> This holy morn is Jesus born!

Christmas day came off with all of the perfection of a birthday party cracker which really exploded when one pulled the tab. Except for a single shadow, that was. For the first time, Grandmother Desmond had been unable to get out for dinner. It was no surprise. Professor Desmond knew his mother had been living on borrowed time for quite a while. But her absence cast a real damper over the table till the telephone rang and the operator announced that it was Seoul, Korea, Lieutenant Desmond calling. Would Professor Desmond accept the charges?

He would, and with a will. Ellen, looking very spruce in her holiday corsage, had, naturally enough, the lion's share of Jack's long distance conversation. Mother came next, and there was just enough room for a few clipped sentences on Father's part before the operator called time. It was the high point of the day for Ellen, Mother, and Father, even if it did mean that, as a result of being distracted from the task in hand, Mother burned the gravy.

Grandfather Hansen's holiday high point was repeated when Kristin again successfully ran through grace at dinner. Moira's and Sheila's high points coincided in two complementary pairs of stilts which, because of the deep snow outside, they tried out in the cellar before dinner. It would be rather difficult to determine what was Karen's high point. It lay between her new noiseless portable typewriter and the Christmas Night dance, to which she went with young Eric Bennett. Rajah and Ranee quite evidently considered the turkey drumsticks, which they later pilfered from the garbage can, their respective high points. As for Kristin, she was still in the paper doll phase. Paper dolls were to her a way of life, if not a compulsion neurosis; and Santa Claus had brought her some perfectly scrumptious ones. Grandaunt Dorothy's high point was, as usual, just being there, able, like some portly fairy godmother, to preside over the table. She was Grandmother Desmond's only sister, and her specialty was telling fortunes for any one who would listen, either by reading tea leaves or dealing cards.

After dinner, the children all gathered round this late Victorian white Witch. Her prognostications were the mixture as before, which is to say that she saw in the leaves and cards the usual satisfactory slathers of lovers, marriages, journeys, and unearned increment. There was one black picture card among the red cards Grandaunt Dorothy turned up. She turned it face down again immediately, without saying a word. For Grandaunt Dorothy, as a haruspicator, functioned on the good old sun-dial principle of numbering only happy hours. It was with a twinge of pain, nevertheless, that Professor Desmond noted his aunt's silent pantomime with the Queen of Spades. He put no faith in the Tarots. But, all the same, he thought he knew for whom that grim fetch had come.

Professor and Mrs. Desmond had their own way of celebrating December thirty-firsts. They let the rest of the world go hang, and stayed home for the evening well fortified with pork sausages, scrambled eggs, a carefully husbanded reserve of good champagne, and some well-chosen books of poetry. Old from the Desmonds' own well-stocked bookshelves; new from those rare nightingales of passage, the review copies of new poetry that, at increasingly fewer stated intervals, winged into a reviewer's eyrie.

Professor Desmond went to one of the living room windows, drew back the flowered drapes, and looked out. The last of December's snow whirled outside the firelit room. Inside, the holiday world was still shrunk to the red round of a Christmas tree ball. It was a fit night for passage and for birthing. A fit night for the two-faced god of January to look before and after, in judgment on the past, in prophecy of the future. A fit night for the little year to enter the dark house of the Weirds for the first time. A night of fantasy. An alchemic night for almanacs and horoscopes, not newspapers or newscasts.

Professor Desmond drew the drapes closed again with a mock shudder.

"Brr!" he said to Toby, laughing.

Toby was curled up on the couch before the fire, Rajah and Ranee at her side, and Sillerton Jackson on a cushion at her feet.

"What are you laughing at, John?" she asked, beginning to laugh herself.

"I've just had a valuable idea, Toby. When I finally go out, I don't want to end either with a bang or a whimper. I want to disappear in a cloud of curious perfume and with a most melodious twang. Do you suppose I could make this a codicil in my will?"

"I don't see why not," said Toby sweetly. "Make a codicil in your will to that effect, I mean. Of course, you'll have to take care of the vanishing trick yourself. Fill up the glasses, dear."

It was a good thing for that weak vessel, man, that there were certain classic ways of keeping the future at bay. The very best of them was to do, as he was now doing — down a judicious amount of bubble and squeak till the zodiacal beasts came down out of their sky and nuzzled one's shoulder.

Professor Desmond raised his glass in the general direction of the angel-inhabited whatnot.

"Skoal!" he said solemnly.

After that toast, he raised his glass again, this time to the Viking ship that sailed across a Christmas sea of greens and red paper elves.

"Skoal!" he said to the Oseberg ship.

Then Professor Desmond proceeded to do a most inconsequential thing.

He burst forth into old Icelandic.

"My word!" said Mother. "What language are you speaking now, John? It sounds positively barbaric."

Professor Desmond looked troubled.

"It is barbaric, Toby," he said. "It's Old Icelandic. From the Saga of Thorfinn Karlsefni who sailed to the New World round about the time of Leif Ericsson. It means that the Indians — if Skraelings are Indians, of course — were frightened by the roaring of the Norseman's bull, and jumped into their canoes and paddled south. And I'm damned if I know what brought it into my mind — haven't thought of it since graduate school days. Do you suppose that, among its many other merits, champagne gives one the power of total recall?"

Mother stretched on the sofa. She had lost interest in the matter.

"I don't know," she said indifferently.

The Chinese are able to tell time by cats' eyes. Ranee, kneading her sharp claws on the Burgundy broadloom, suddenly leaped onto the sofa and fixed her arrogant blue orbs squarely on Mother's brown ones. Just then the whistles started blowing outside.

There is no irony like the irony of a woman who both loves and understands a man.

"Has my lord dallied with poetry among the roses?" asked Mother slily. "Sufficiently long, that is, to put an edge on his royal appetite for his first snack of the new year?"

Professor Desmond looked at her accusingly.

"That's the Queen to Taliessin," he said. "In Charles Williams' Region of the Summer Stars. I gave it to you for your birthday. You're plagiarizing."

Mother kissed him.

"Of course it is," she said. "Of course you did. Of course I'm not. I'm quoting. It all goes to prove I read my birthday presents."

He kissed her back.

"Speaking of kissing," said Professor Desmond after an interval. "How old is young Kevin down the street?"

"Five," said Mother.

"Well, keep an eye on him," said Professor Desmond, releasing her. "Kristin tells me he laughs, kisses, and is a strong fighter. If that isn't the definition of a great lover, I don't know one."

The table was set with Mother's Royal Danish silver, and her Copenhagen china. Father's Royal Doulton Falstaff, a surprise present from Mother and the children, stood on the candle-flanked glass mirror in the middle. The fat knight's doublet was soft rose in the mellow light. His arms akimbo, he seemed to wink as the Swedish flying angel candelabra on the sideboard gained momentum, one brass angel following close on the cherub heels of the others. Back in the living room, on the long-play, Frankie Carle alternated with Xavier Cugat, for the Desmonds had every bit as great a weakness for short-hair as for long-hair music. The bells and whistles did not stop for a full quarter of an hour.

Professor Desmond put down his fork with a sigh of contentment.

"Another thing," he said, harking back to Kevin. "That brother and sister of Kevin's. The ones Moira and Sheila are always playing with. I don't know if they're a good influence. They always say *git* instead of *get*. And only yesterday I heard them shouting at the Duncan kids next door."

"What did they shout, John?" asked Mother patiently. She rather liked the little Callahans.

"They shouted: *Protestants stink! Protestants stink!*"

Professor Desmond stopped and thought a moment.

"That's not good," he concluded rather lamely.

"No, John, I agree," said Mother. "That's not good. Did they have provocation?"

"Well, yes," said Professor Desmond. "Now that I think of it, I remember that the little Duncans had been shouting: *Catholics stink!*"

"I hope Moira and Sheila didn't join in," said Mother.

Then Professor Desmond began to laugh.

"No, they didn't," he said. "When I complimented them they said they couldn't, because their Grandfather was one."

"One what?" asked Mother, puzzled.

"A Protestant," said Professor Desmond, beginning to laugh very hard now. "Happy New Year, Toby!"

Time was: Time is: Time is not, runs the rune. Upstairs, just as the whistles went midnight, Karen had a curious dream. She was in a waiting crowd which danced and sang in the narrow streets

of a strange town. They were all dressed in old-fashioned clothes —
she herself, for example, had on a green kirtle with a silver belt. Yet
everything was real, not a masquerade. They had left a space free
in the middle of the principal street, which wound down from a
sort of castle on a hill to the side of the water. Suddenly a great
roar of voices, drawing closer every second, gave notice that the
expected ones were coming. Then, preceded by lighted torches,
they came, several hundred strong. A Jarl in silver armor, whose
face seemed queerly familiar to the sleeping girl — and yet she
was awake, too, in a way — and his Viking followers. They were
parading to the shore. Shouting, the people followed them. There
was a ship drawn up on the edge of the strand. A dead warrior, his
white beard lying quiet on his breast outside his chainmail, sat with
his back to the high mast. His treasures were drawn up around him:
silver coins and gold rings, dragon-hilted swords and curiously
wrought brooches. Somehow, Karen knew that the dead man was
the Jarl's father.

The young chieftain in the silver mail took a torch from one
of the attendants, strode up to the ship, and thrust the blazing
link into the prow. Twelve of his warriors followed suit. Then the
attendants pushed the burning craft on rollers out into the bay. It
was all aflame now, all but the sail with the red serpent on it.
The Vikings raised their swords and shouted. The townspeople took
up the shout after them. Karen found herself crying out with the
rest. Crying out something that sounded like: *Up Hella Aa!* But, in
the morning, she could not really remember just what it had sounded
like. The pictures remained clear, though, for it had been a most
compelling dream. It stayed with her for several days. Then, as
dreams do, it faded again, but not before she realized that the young
Jarl of her dream looked like the Viking masquerader at Jack's
Halloween party.

CHAPTER FIVE

Will You No' Come Back Again?

GREAT-AUNT Dorothy's Queen of Spades turned up again. Spring was less than three weeks old when Deborah Desmond died.

The long low funeral coach swung away from the Desmond family plot at Limestone Hill, and, gaining momentum as it left the cemetery gates, turned first right, then sharp left, and onto McKinley Parkway. As usual, the recessional away from the grave seemed a thing of breakneck speed after the slow processional from church to graveside. A fine April rain began to fall. After several days of sunny weather, there was a chill in the air again. The windshield wipers swished liquidly across the glass.

No one of the three older children spoke. Ellen stared straight ahead, her thoughts thousands of miles away with Jack in Korea. Mother looked at Father. Professor Desmond sat stony-faced, white, his right hand clutching the upholstered strap that hung down alongside the left-hand window. She felt an illimitable remoteness in him. And a hardness like that of some pebble withdrawn and alone on a beach with thousands of other pebbles. He was not in the car at all. He was not even back at the grave of his mother, where the diggers were already tamping down the last turves over the coffin of Deborah Desmond, aetat. eighty-three, housewife, widow for better than a quarter of a century, beloved mother and grandmother. He was somewhere in the arid spaces of desolation, and moving further away every second. With the wiseness of women who love, Mrs. Desmond knew that this involuntary withdrawal could become voluntary; that there was a danger of willfulness and perversity in her husband's sudden grief, the more startling because he had given no evidence of being so affected during the long days and nights of the wake.

When the automobile reached Seneca Street, Professor Desmond reached forward and tapped the driver on the shoulder. His voice was stiff and formal and carefully precise. It did not bother the driver in the slightest. This was the way some of them always behaved on the way back. Chattered like magpies all the way to the cemetery. Then clammed up utterly on the road home. Not all of them, of course. But a good many. It was a standard enough reaction.

"Down Seneca to Delaware, please," said Professor Desmond, enunciating each separate syllable with the most painful clarity. "Then over Delaware to Ferry Street. The children and Mrs. Desmond will get off at the *Campanile*, at their grandfather's apartment. Then you may take me back to the house."

It was done. A small thing, but it had required an almost infinite act of the will to resist the paralysis that had been closing in on him ever since the end of his mother's Requiem Mass. It was the first small step on the road back to the consoling, deadening, merciful minutiae of every day. He did not feel any better, though. The constriction was not lifting from his chest.

The bad time had set in just after the Last Gospel when the celebrant laid aside his chasuble and maniple and, vested in his black cope, came, attended by deacon and subdeacon, to the foot of the bier, where the subdeacon left him.

His eyes blurring, a son listened to the great promise made to his mother:

"I am the resurrection and the life: he that believeth in Me, although he be dead, shall live: and every one who liveth, and believeth in Me, shall never die."

On went the measured chanting, rising and falling, and Professor Desmond only felt himself become harder and drier and further removed.

"Requiescat in pace."
"A portis inferi."

The celebrant put incense in the thurifer.

"*Pater noster*," he intoned.

He passed around the bier twice, incensing it and sprinkling it with holy water.

"A *portis inferi*."

"*Requiescat in pace*."

As he retreated further and further away from the points of light the candles burning about the coffin made, Professor Desmond could feel that his wife sensed this withdrawal; that she feared it; that she desperately wanted him to return. And he knew suddenly that merely willing a return would not help. He had to come to terms with himself in silence and alone. He had to talk things out with no one present but himself.

He let himself into the empty house with his front door key. The undertaker's men had "cleaned up" according to their lights, which meant no more than that they had carried off the flower baskets, the green strips of matting, and the folding chairs. The carpet was strewn with flower petals. The room felt cold, because, during the wake, the thermostat had been turned down to sixty-two. Now, the incense smell still gritty in his nostrils, walking on dead and dying rose leaves, he turned it up again to seventy. Then, crumpling some newspaper and disposing some bark kindling in the fireplace, he set some logs crosswise and touched a match to them. Fire was a living, elemental thing. It warmed the heart as well as the hands. It would help a little. For the first time in years, it seemed, he sat down and relaxed.

His mother's had been a good death — if there was such a thing as a good death. Maybe a house needed a death in it, every bit as much as it needed a birth. Maybe it needed a grave-ale as well as a christening-ale. Maybe a house was not complete before one of the dear dead belonged to it forever. Maybe. If so, it had its death now. A house was a triune unity of hearth and table and bed. A house was love. A house was *pietas*, love's recognition and acknowledgment. It was love and *pietas* that, in the end, held mankind together.

Already the house seemed friendly again. Say, rather, friendlier. Even when the cypress was on the lintel, when the golden bowl was broken, and the silver thread just snapped, it had never been anything but friendly. But there are occasions for a house, even as there are occasions for man. Sometimes a house must be stately, not cozy. Now it was growing cozy once again. He listened to the comfortable house noises. The low hum of the furnace fan after the gas heat snapped on. The curious yearning note in the mechanical snarl of the tame dinosaur that was the electric refrigerator. Good genii, both of them. Hewers of wood and drawers of water for mechanized man in the age of anxiety. The tightness in his chest began to lift. But not all the way. Something more was needed still.

Suddenly a strong wave of love went out from Professor Desmond toward his mother, toward this house of theirs that had so many of her things in it, toward that other little house she had helped him buy, waking now under the April rain over on the Canadian shore. Where was his mother now? At rest, in peace, in eternity, in heaven, entered into life. What did the formulae mean? As well say in fairyland as in paradise. As well say in Arthur's as in Abraham's bosom. In both places one should be happy forever and ever. In both places should be slaked and cooled the burning primordial desires of dream and story. So ran the great promise of the New Testament. But did a person ever really believe the great promise?

It was appropriate that his mind should run on fairy tales. His mother had liked to read to him and, afterward, when he could read, to buy him fairy tales. She had made him free, early in life, of the cinque ports of Faërie: Grimm, Andersen, the Arabian Nights, the great Lang collections, the legends of Greece and Scandinavia and ancient Ireland. Now she, too, had gone through the looking glass. *Finish, good lady, the bright day is done, And we are for the dark.* Or was the night not dark for her? Was it that, on the other side of the looking glass, she no longer saw through a glass darkly? Had she lifted the blanket of the dark only to find under it a counterpane of light? If there was such a thing as another dimension, surely his mother was in another — no, *the* other — dimension. The one just around the corner in time and space. At the back of the north wind. East of the sun, west of the moon. One reached it in life for fleeting visits now and then. Through a rabbit hole, a rose garden, a nursery wardrobe, an attic room where lay long forgotten books. Through memories of childhood. The first Christmas tree, the first Easter basket, the first birthday party. Through first love.

Through great poetry. Its final vestibule was death. And what finally lay at the end of the corridor?

Before that came the little deaths. Cocktail parties, social martyrdoms, family reunions patiently endured. That most tremendous of all family reunions — more tremendous than weddings, even — a wake. In spite of himself, Professor Desmond began to smile a little. Wakes! He had promised his mother she should be waked in the good old Irish fashion; and he had fulfilled his promise. In one way, it had not been so bad, really. Like so many other things in life, wakes were at once a weariness of the flesh and high comedy. Sometimes low comedy as well. Except for death. There was no comedy in death.

Death, thought Professor Desmond, wasn't a very progressive idea. It was the most stubbornly reactionary fact man ever came up against. He often wondered if, in the end, one didn't just go down into a great darkness. To gain salvation, they said, one had to believe as a child. The trouble was that, even as a child, he had not been able to believe as a child. The difference between him and most of those who disbelieved was that, as a Catholic, he was committed to belief. As a result, he simultaneously believed and disbelieved. He believed with the top of his mind. He doubted with his blood. But his mother, who had had so few illusions, had believed. His mother had been disillusioned, but never disenchanted.

No, his mother had never felt the way he did about death. Death to her was, if not exactly an old friend, at any rate the most intimate of acquaintances. That was a point of view his generation could no longer share. The idea of God was by no means dead in the twentieth century. In some ways, it was actually more alive than it had been in the preceding hundred years. But the idea of personal immortality, of survival of the individual human personality after death, was definitely less vivid. It had never actually been as strong as the idea of God. Intimations of deity pressed one about on every side. One did not have this same imaginative conviction about the resurrection of the body. One believed, perhaps. If one was lucky. One never felt sure in one's bones. Not even the ancient Hebrews. Not even the old Egyptians, really. Not even the people of the high Christian ages. Only that strange people, the Irish, the people of the dead. The people to whom his mother had belonged. Even in Druidic days the Irish had been confident that they should live again.

Professor Desmond put another log on the fire. He was beginning to relax now. There was no real sense of death in the house, nor had there been in the three days his mother's body had rested, light, poised, curiously young; aloof but not distant, either, before his mantel. He remembered many things, and his memories were without grief for the moment. He remembered how she had loved animals and cemeteries and churches; how, for the past ten years, Deborah Desmond had gone downhill slowly, surely, valiantly. She died sometime between six and seven in the morning, full of years and love and laughter.

Five sons mourned her — one had gone before. Twenty-five grandchildren; sixteen great-grandchildren. Twelve priests, one of them her oldest grandchild, sang her passing. Three Bishops blessed her that the thunder and lightning of hell gate might not daunt this old Irish woman who looked so young again in her blue shroud. Her wake was as gay as herself. She had been not proud; nor very meek, either. She had been uniquely, lovably, eternally — herself.

There — he had said it at last. Eternally. So, after all, he did believe. Not as a child believes, it was true. But sufficiently. He was content.

Professor Desmond put his head back on the couch.

When, around five in the afternoon, Mrs. Desmond let herself in the front door, the annealing process had already gone a long way. Her husband was asleep on the couch, his first really untroubled sleep in a week. There were some things more important, though, than sleep. She hung up her worn wrap and muff, tiptoed over to the fire, then woke him with a kiss.

"I've something to tell you, John," she said.

"Yes?"

He sat up, yawning, hair tousled.

"I went over to the Medical Center Building with Ellen," she said.

"Yes?" he said again, stupid with sleep.

"There's going to be a baby, John," she said.

"Oh," he said. "Never noticed it. Funny she didn't tell us before.

It must be well along by now."

Mother sat down beside him.

"Not Ellen, John," she said. "Us."

Professor Desmond sat bolt upright.

"Good God!" he said explosively. "Us! No — we!"

"Us," she said. "Let it be us, John, this once."

Then Mother began to laugh. She laughed as Sara, Abraham's wife, had laughed in secret behind the door of her tent when she heard the Lord promise Abraham that she should bear a son. And she had Sara in mind, too. For she curtsied, still laughing, and said:

"*After I am grown old and my lord is an old man, shall I give myself to pleasure? And Sara said to herself: God hath made a laughter for me. Whosoever shall hear of it will laugh with me.*"

Professor Desmond looked at his wife with admiration.

"Never mind that old man stuff," he said. "But just when did you start boning up on the Bible, Toby?"

"Last week," she said. "When I was pretty sure."

"I'll cap your quote," he said. "From Shakespeare."

Professor Desmond plucked a complete Shakespeare from one of the two fireside book alcoves and riffled the pages till he came to the end of *A Midsummer Night's Dream.*

"Listen to this, Toby," he said. "Puck and Oberon. And Sara. Now we've got profane as well as sacred love.

"First from Puck:

> *And we fairies that do run*
> > *By the triple Hecate's team,*
> *From the presence of the sun,*
> > *Following darkness like a dream,*
> *Now are frolic: not a mouse*
> *Shall disturb this hallow'd house.*
> *I am sent with broom before,*
> > *To sweep the dust behind the door.*"

"Oh, John," she said. "That's lovely."

"Wait a minute," he said. "There's Oberon to come. Listen:

> *Now, until the break of day,*
> *Through the house each fairy stray.*

To the best bride-bed will we,
Which by us will blessed be;
And the issue there create
Ever shall be fortunate."

Professor Desmond laid the book down. "Well?" he said.

"It's very nice, John," she said. "It's also the only time I can remember ever liking that horrid word, 'issue.' But, John, I'm hardly a bride after all these years."

Like many Irishmen, when Professor Desmond grew gallant, he grew rough. His silken tongue was reserved for the elegance of courtly insult.

"You're a hell of a lot better than a bride," he said.

It was always the enchanted wood nearby that made men's mortal doings sweeter. The dam was broken. The ice around his heart had thawed. While Mother got dinner in the kitchen, she heard him in the study, humming the old Jacobite air he loved so well, the one that must be sung in the melting Northumbrian of Yorkshire and the Scottish Lowlands, and of his father's Ulster:

"Better lo'ed you canna be, will you no' come back again?"

Next morning, at breakfast, it was the mixture as before. Rajah ate a bran muffin, which was not a usual thing for a cat to eat. Ranee ate three soda crackers, which were hardly ordinary cat's fare, either. But, then, it was a moot point whether Siamese were really cats. Kristin had cut out a sequence of miniature paper ties which had come through the mail to Professor Desmond. One by one, she put them on Bozo.

"What kind of a tie is this?" she asked her father.

Professor Desmond raised his eyes from the sport page.

"A Hubert de Givenchy," he said with decision. "Very swank, too. Bozo looks a real man of distinction."

Kristin held up another.

"This one?" she asked.

"I believe," said Professor Desmond, folding up the paper, "that one is a Countess Mara. The next is a Sulka."

"This one?" said Kristin.

Professor Desmond squinted at it.

"As I live and breathe," he said. "A clutch of swans. That, my poppet, can be nothing short of a Bronzini."

He picked up a sheet of paper that had come with the ties.

"My Lord, Toby!" he said, awed. "Listen to this color list: hibiscus red, pale apricot, Aubusson pink, wisteria, café au lait, Parma violet. For heaven's sake, try to moderate Bozo's sartorial transports. We don't want him whistled at."

"You manage to moderate your own sartorial transports quite successfully, John," said Mrs. Desmond sweetly. "As a matter of fact, I think you could do quite nicely with a dash of Parma violet."

Professor Desmond bolted a second coffee and snatched up his briefcase.

"What kind of a tie have you got on, Dad?" Kristin asked him at the door.

"Oh, I don't know, Krissie," he said, puzzled. "Just a tie, I guess."

Mother smiled.

"I'll tell you, Kristin," she said. "The tie your father is wearing is the one on the outside of his tie rack. The one nearest his hand. I know. I rotate them every week. And he never knows the difference."

Among the letters of condolence was one from Gottfried Krehan, who had come by accident on the newspaper account of Deborah Desmond's death in the *Cosmos Club* copy of the *Buffalo Courier Express*. No one but a professional at the game could have told that the envelope had been steamed open and then sealed again. Mr. Tikjan's Desmond dossier was beginning to grow.

CHAPTER SIX

~~~~~~

Return to Summer

THE months resumed their march. Sheila became nine. Kristin would be five soon; and, in a matter of months, Moira could call herself eleven. But — to Karen, at least — her fifteenth birthday still seemed aeons off.

Lazily the American earth stirred, stretched, shook itself, then turned over again in one last late winter sleep. The spring earth in America was sleazily untidy, a masculine thing; a sempiternal Huckleberry Finn grown old, no classic Pan; a river god, not a woodland goddess. After a spell, it sat up foggily and, ruminating, rubbed the gray-rimed pussy willow stubble on its chin. Thunder yawned a soft accompaniment.

As the spring thunder muttered sleepily overhead, the light bulbs dimmed on Hurst Monceux Boulevard, and the dim green dusk of April came flooding into Kristin's bedroom, darkening the clown night lamp that burned beside her on the table. Kristin did not like the smoky grain of the thundery light.

"Dad," she called, "I'm afraid. I'm afraid in the dark. I want Bozo."

Patiently Professor Desmond rounded up that orange-topped talisman of talismans and carried it in to his young daughter.

"There," he said, tucking Bozo in beside her. "Now everything is all right."

"Yes," said Kristin. "I don't have to be afraid now. I've got Bozo, Elizabeth, Caspar the Friendly Ghost, and God."

"Why put God last?" asked Professor Desmond.

"Because he's visible," said Kristin.

"Invisible, Kristin," said Professor Desmond irritably. "Not visible. *Visible* means something you can see. *Invisible* means you can't see it. But you can't see Caspar, either. Caspar's a phonograph record."

"Oh, yes I can," said Kristin, hauling out a slate from underneath her covers. "Moira drew him for me."

"O.K.," said Professor Desmond, routed. "You can see Caspar. Now get to sleep."

Just then the thunder cracked directly overhead. The child whimpered a little, then got control of herself.

"I laugh at the thunder," she said bravely.

Valiant is the word for Kristin, thought Professor Desmond, as he walked downstairs again. When you got right down to it, lightning scared the living bejabers out of him, though he could hardly admit it. But he had spoken prematurely.

"Dad!" Kristin called again.

Professor Desmond walked back upstairs with excessively bad grace.

"What's the matter now?" he said.

"I don't like the storm," said Kristin.

"Look," said Professor Desmond. "There's nothing to worry about. You've got God, Queen Elizabeth, Bozo, and Caspar. What more do you need?"

"That's four," said Kristin. "I need five."

"Hell!" said Professor Desmond hopelessly.

He went out into the hall. There was a toy monkey on the landing. He picked it up and gave it to her.

"There," he said. "Now that's all. You get to sleep."

"Dad," said Kristin, as he was closing the door. "Come here a minute."

Professor Desmond's bark was considerably worse than his bite. He opened the door wide again and walked over to the little bed.

"Well," he said. "What's the matter this time?"

"Do you want to see something lovely in fur?" asked Kristin.

"I suppose so," said Professor Desmond. "Show me something lovely in fur."

She held up the monkey.

"How do you do, Jocko," said Professor Desmond, bowing formally and kissing them both.

Number five seemed to work. There was no further protest from the little bed. The thunder grumbled off in the distance.

Across the river the Canadian earth prepared itself for Spring's visitation. It was tidier, tardier, chaster than the American earth. Loons called in Georgian Bay. Salmon girded for their mighty swim upstream. Against the weathered gray of the Desmonds' Crescent Beach garage, with the black paint flecking off the letters on the name-board, a lilac's purple mist made a Japanese composition.

Spring came early to Sheridan Circle where ramped the bronze horseman on his brazen horse. For the hundredth time Dr. Krehan stood in the Circle, this time poking the gold-green pollen balls along the pavement with his cane, and thinking on the problem of the bronze horsemen. Bronze horsemen were much alike, whether one came upon them in Berlin's *Sieges Allee*, in a Paris square, or here, in this Southern city of magnolias, Washington.

In Buffalo, four hundred and twenty miles to the north of Sheridan Circle, Professor Desmond, who had fought in France, and in his day, pondered another bronze horseman. It was one of Professor Desmond's more sentimental gestures to load the children into the car and tour the city's statues on Decoration Day. Memorial Day it read on most of the calendars nowadays. They still said Decoration Day in Buffalo, just as in his boyhood. Only last month he had heard a boy ask on an April bus: "When is it? Decoration Day, I mean."

But not all the children. Karen was too old, and Kristin too young, for this sort of sentimental journey. They cramped his style at both ends of the emotional spectrum. And not all the statues, either. Only the appropriate ones. The soldiers and sailors, in their honored patina of green, on Lafayette Square. The Cooper Indian in Delaware Park. The young Lincoln in front of the Rose Gardens, one statue down from Michelangelo's David, where the Buffalo lovers parked under the heroic fig leaf, the ornamental, lamplit little lake between them, David, and Lincoln. The new equestrian statue of General Daniel Bidwell on the round grass plot in Colonial Circle.

Sitting there on the last of May's new grass, beneath the bronze horseman's patient spurs, Sheila and Moira forged their yellow chains of dandelion gold. When one was done, they presented it to their father. Professor Desmond took it from them gravely and, when they went back to the statue's base, meditatively bit into the linked stems. The dandelion was bitter brass and iron to the tongue. Not bronze, brass. Bronze was bitter enough, but, like bitter laurel, bronze was the taste of victory, not defeat. This tasted iron, like slavers' manacles. Brass, like cartridges bitten off in the Wilderness. Like Minie balls teeth-clenched while surgeons probed, after Cedar Creek where Bidwell fought.

Professor Desmond read the inscription on the pediment overhead. If bronze horses and bronze horsemen were much alike the world over, so were all wars men died in much alike. Patroclus was as cold — no more, no less — as Private First Class Dudzik: *In Korea*. For those who died — if not for those who lived — it was all one war. For those who lived, there was their war and the wars of others. Your war was the war you fought in. No one could take that war from you. Nor could anyone — not even a son — give you his war. Professor Desmond thought he pitied the men who had not fought in any war. They were even as childless women were.

But were all wars men died in really so much alike? Surely Bidwell's war had been somehow different. It still ached in him along his American bone. Buffalo was older than the War Between the States. The British burned it in 1813. At the time of the Revolution — and before that, as early, even, as the year Wolfe stormed Quebec — the British had held Fort Niagara. And before them the French. But the Revolution did not make the short hairs rise on Professor Desmond's neck, when he thought on it. The Civil War did. At this far remove in time, the Revolution was fancy clothes. A jaunty feather in a doodle hat. Toy centerpieces for February 22. Souvenirs at Fort Niagara. Pageant wigs. Grease paint and rouge, not blood and sweat and death.

Bidwell's war was the archetype: brother against brother. But not Cain against Abel. No, wars were never quite so clear-cut as all that. Say, rather, Abel against Abel. Or, depending on your philosophy, Cain against Cain. Thunder growled yet in those dark thunderheads of time: 1861, 1864, 1865. These battles would never be far off and long ago. Not for Americans. There was defeat as well as victory in them. They were the only war Americans, in winning, ever lost.

Mostly, though, Professor Desmond said fiercely to himself, we won. That was the sowing. The seeds were iron, and the harrows. The harvest came later: bronze and marble bloom. That border acre, Gettysburg, bloomed first and best. No other battlefield could match its monumental harvest. He must see it again. And this time the children were old enough to see it with him. They could do it in August, after summer school was over. They could, and, by George, they would! It was time the kids saw a little of the South.

It was growing chill as the sun came down. General Bidwell's green-bronze began to turn gray-steel in the dusk. Professor Desmond got to his feet with a yawn that was half a sigh.

When they came in, three quarters of an hour late, Mother had the boiled tongue already on the table.

"Achtung!" said Professor Desmond, to cover up their delinquency. "Cold cuts again!"

"Joke!" she said to him coldly. "And not a particularly good one. What's more, I read it in the undergraduate paper last week. Besides, the tongue's hot — or was a half hour ago. Help set the table, while the girls wash up."

After supper Professor Desmond retreated to a pipe and easy chair. He put a record of Nat King Cole's on the long play and settled back. He liked Debussy and he liked jazz. Nat King Cole could make jazz sound like Debussy's *Arabesques*, each note as round and perfect and separate as an abstract raindrop.

Upstairs Moira's radio cut across his Nat King Cole long play.

"Moira!" he called from his chair. "Have you finished your homework for tomorrow?"

"I'm doing it now," called back Moira.

"Turn off the radio then," he said.

The rival boogie-woogie stopped.

Professor Desmond got out of his easy chair.

"What's your task?" he called up the stairwell.

Moira came to the banister.

"It's for English composition," she said. "Sister Helen told us to write down what we could remember of some dinner table conversation during the week."

"Good God!" said Professor Desmond, irritated. "What for? I

consider that kind of assignment as much an invasion of my personal privacy as wire-tapping."

"So we can help make next week's dinner table conversation more stimulating," said Moira.

"It's stimulating enough now," said Professor Desmond. "If it gets any more stimulating, we'll all have ulcers. What night are you writing up?"

"Last Thursday night," said Moira.

Professor Desmond quickly ransacked his memories. As far as he could remember — which was not very far — last Thursday night had not been any different from any other night at the Desmond table.

"What happened Thursday?" he asked Moira.

"That was the night we had the pot roast," said Moira "You were late coming to the table."

Professor Desmond was always late coming to the table. He did not think the fact particularly worthy of incorporation in a composition.

"Read me what you've written down," he said.

Moira squatted on the top step.

" 'After,' " she read, " 'we had finished our Lutheran grace in Norwegian, Daddy finally came to the table. When he saw it was pot roast, he said he needed some white wine. So he went back to his study and brought out a bottle which, being imported, needed a corkscrew. After five minutes trying, he put the corkscrew down, and went back to the study again to get an American bottle. The tops screw off American bottles, so he didn't need a corkscrew. By the time he came back, Mother had got the cork out of the other bottle. The pot roast was cold. My Daddy is not very good with tools.' "

Professor Desmond laughed.

"That's playing it straight anyway," he said. "Do you think, though, that Sister Helen is going to find this very edifying, Moira? Besides, you use 'needed' too many times for one paragraph."

Professor Desmond went back to his brooding. He brooded now on the spiritual order; especially on that part of it which could be summed up as parochial organization.

Sometimes Professor Desmond wondered — his wife could have told him the answer — if there weren't something almost too arrogantly patrician in his make-up to allow him to stomach the excesses of parochial organization. If he could be said to have aristocratic tastes, certainly the Mass, with its dramatic grandeur, its ritual ballet of celebrant and server, its blazing, more than operatic climax of the Consecration, should satisfy those tastes. And, as a matter of fact, the Mass did, no matter how awkward, no matter how poised the celebrant. The Mass never put him off. It was the carnival barker, the geeks outside; the tawdry shops next to French Canadian shrines. Tawdry, he reflected grimly, came from St. Audrey. Evidently this was an old, old problem in the Church. And it wasn't getting solved very rapidly. Lotteries, chances, bingo when bingo was legal, near bingo when straight bingo was outlawed. Bread and circuses outside the House of Bread. It was all too close to that bad legacy of Latin origin, that awful marijuana of the poor, that opium of the peon — the pinchbeck paradise of numbered paper. And the children picked it up only too readily. Picked it up? Hell! They had it foisted on them in the very classroom. It was, he thought, a terrible perversion of the sacred teaching function, this debasing of the real currency of spiritual experience with the tinsel heaven of the numbers game. Was it a law of existence that all collective enterprise should, in some way or other, eventually become tarnished? Perhaps mendicant orders were necessary — he raised no question about that. But he was not bringing up his children to be mendicants.

Then there was this maddening mission Great-aunt Dorothy had imposed upon him, as he put her on the train for California two weeks after Grandmother Desmond's funeral. She had thrust into his hands a wicker bottle of the sort that one associated with pictures of Don Quixote and Sancho Panza. It was no new thing in his life, that Rabelaisian Oracle of the Bottle which Great-aunt Dorothy had brought back from Lourdes in the early Twenties. It had been full then and, like the miraculous pitcher, it never seemed to run dry, though Great-aunt Dorothy was in the habit of dispensing liberal pint measures of it to all and sundry among her ailing friends and acquaintances — and the friends of her friends, too, to say nothing of the acquaintances of her acquaintances.

"Get this to Harry Finnegan's wife," she said. "She's dying."

Miserably he had balanced the bottle on the train platform.

"But Aunt Dorothy," he said, "the bottle must be empty by now. You brought it back from Lourdes over thirty years ago."

"Twenty-nine," she corrected him. "Shake it. It's more than half full."

So it was. He shook it, and it gurgled.

"How come?" said Professor Desmond, flabergasted.

"I refill it every month," said Great-aunt Dorothy.

"You what — ?" said Professor Desmond.

"Oh, yes," said Aunt Dorothy. "Otherwise it would be dry in no time."

In no time! This caper, said Professor Desmond to himself, was outside of time altogether. So, sometimes, was Great-aunt Dorothy.

"But," he said, "then it's no longer holy water. It's only plain ordinary tap water."

"Oh, no, John," said Great-aunt Dorothy sweetly. "It's holy water all right."

"But how in hell — ?" began Professor Desmond.

"It blesses itself," said Great-aunt Dorothy.

The engine hissed clouds of steam. "Bo-o-o-a-r-d!" called the conductor. Professor Desmond did not hear him. Holding the great muleteer's bottle cradled in both arms, he heard, instead, across the remembered escaping steam of three decades, the Pyrenean conductor of a *voiture locale* crying out: "*En vo-i-t-u-r-r-e!*" as Great-aunt Dorothy left the little Basque capital forever, laden with rosaries, scapulars, and an immense wicker bottle; an aunt of aunts, dumpy and indomitable, like the balloon woman in Rackham's *Peter Pan*; earth-bound, hell-bent for heaven. She was still, after all these years, earth-bound and heaven-bent, and singularly unbattered by her friendly enemy, old time.

Nat King Cole had long since switched himself off and Professor Desmond was dozing in his chair, when the children came into the living room to kiss him good night.

Mr. Tikjan was encountering his own frustrations. Mr. Tikjan was a humble votary of history — a voluntary eunuch of her harem, as it were. He could discharge her orders. He could not anticipate her moods. Above all, he could not predict when she might take it into her mind to change her costume, as, pouting prettily, she chose to do on this June day.

The Communist Party in America found itself suddenly squeezed between the lobster claws of two quite different pincers. Without warning, the F.B.I. cracked down on cell leaders in strategic areas throughout the nation. Even more drastically, with the downfall of Lavrenti Beria, world Communism found itself faced with the perennial dilemma of all conspiratorial states. Who would guard the guards? What underground agency could be trusted to certify the inverted loyalty of the professionally disloyal? The men of the M.V.D. in America, as elsewhere, had been Beria's men, members of his private Pretorian guard. With Beria gone, did the local M.V.D. men still possess authority? Membership cards were called in and hastily scrutinized A wave of impromptu liquidations disrupted the organizational harmony of the Washington *Apparat* to which Mr. Tikjan was accredited.

Mr. Tikjan's single passion, aside from his work, was a cosmopolitan attachment to the richer varieties of food. Now, all of a sudden, he found himself with unlimited time on his hands in which to gratify this pleasantest of hobbies. There was a complete and inexplicable breach of contact between him and the man immediately above him in the *Apparat*. It was all most distressing. Mr. Tikjan's tidy little soul did not like to leave a job undone. Besides, he sensed that Dr. Krehan's importance to the Communist scheme of things was growing rather than diminishing; that it was, in fact, just about to start. But, in his own way, Mr. Tikjan was both a practical philosopher and a good Party man. He knew that a Communist agent did not think for himself. A Communist agent waited for orders. So, like the faithful centurion of the New Testament, Mr. Tikjan, too, sat back and waited for orders.

Twice a day he put in a discreet appearance both at the great fountain in the Mellon Gallery, and just in front of the glass case that was labeled *Cunningham Skink* in the Washington Zoo's Reptile House, both of which were places where his superior had been in the habit of meeting him at stated intervals. Once a man on a bus got up just as Mr. Tikjan was sitting down, leaving on the seat behind him a newspaper open to the crossword puzzle. It was a dodge Mr. Tikjan had seen worked before. He closely examined the puzzle to see if there were any message blocked in for him. The white squares were virgin of any markings whatsoever. It must have been only a coincidence. On another occasion, he followed a man he had never seen before because, just as Mr. Tikjan approached his regular bus stop, the man waiting on the corner — ostentatiously, or so it seemed — dropped a cigarette from his left hand and carefully stubbed it into the gravel with his left foot. Then he walked slowly and invitingly away. This gesture, too, in Mr. Tikjan's curious trade, was a cabalistic ensign. But not, as it happened, in this case. Mr. Tikjan spent a hot and frustrating forenoon fruitlessly trailing a blind lead about the grounds and through the imitation catacombs of the Franciscan Monastery.

After one interminable week of such false starts Mr. Tikjan gave up this particular ghost. Mahomet had failed. Let the mountain now come to Mahomet, he said to himself. Meanwhile he would indulge himself by playing sybarite in the restaurants of his choice. The restaurants of his choice tended to be prevalently Middle Eastern, though he also had a weakness for the fare of that Eastern enclave which used to be old Vienna; for coffee with stiff-whipped *Schlagobers* and flakily crisp *Kaisersemmeln*.

America, incidentally, seemed to have contributed only one thing to the gratification of Mr. Tikjan's idiosyncratic palate: the confection known as chocolate turtles. The affinity may have been psychic as well as gustatory. If one looked closely, one might decide that, with his dark facial planes and fleshy toucan's beak, Mr. Tikjan looked not at all unlike a chocolate turtle himself.

History, in her gayest carnival domino, put a gold-chased lorgnette to her eye and watched Mr. Tikjan through the quizzing glass. The little man amused her. Then she trained the lens on the 16th of June strikers in Berlin.

On the night of the 17th, Ernst Reuter, ox-shouldered Mayor of West Berlin, pushed the French beret he always wore back on his head, and wrote to his old friend, Herr Doktor Gottfried Krehan, care of the *Klub Kosmos*, Washington, D. C.

Lieber Gottfried:

Perhaps the hour strikes sooner than we once thought. But that is something we can talk about this fall, after the September

*elections, when you come to visit me at last. I can promise you
some rather good international fare. Salade — French. A piping
bowl of katscha soup — Russian, and far better than that over-rated
borscht. An evening of Theocritus — Greek, you will remember.
And, to top it all off, a little echt Gemütlichkeit — Deutsch, no
one can take this away from us.*

In the meanwhile . . .

Mr. Tikjan got to see this letter; and it led him to a serious and,
in point of fact, unprecedented decision. Mr. Tikjan was not in the
habit of reading the political news very much. Besides, the really
important political news had a way of not getting printed. He did
not know, for example, that the Western allies were considering
dusting off the old Locarno Pact idea. That Chancellor Adenauer
was seriously pondering the feasibility of tucking it into his platform
for the September elections. That there had been conversations between Adenauer and Mayor Reuter concerning the desirability of
bringing back Gottfried Krehan to help hammer out the legal in-
strument that might one day be the new Locarno. Soviet intelligence
knew all the relevant facts about the possible new move but one.
They did not yet know Krehan's projected part in it. The Reuter
letter could provide them with the missing pieces in the puzzle. One
of the Kremlin factions wanted a new Locarno; another did not.
Once Krehan's putative role was known to this latter faction, his
life — or, at least, his liberty — would not be worth a month's pur-
chase. Mr. Tikjan could not possibly be aware of these currents and
counter-currents. All he felt was a pricking in his thumb of prophecy
in Dr. Krehan's regard.

Meditatively slipping back the envelope into its proper place, after
reading it, Mr. Tikjan came to what was for him an absolutely rev-
olutionary conclusion. For once, he would act on his own. Since,
in its turn, the mountain had failed to come to Mahomet, it now
behooved Mahomet to go direct to the mountain. In this case, of
course, the mountain was New York City, American Communism's
Mecca, as Washington was its Bagdad.

The day Mr. Tikjan brought his unsolicited news to the Workers
Bookshop, on the ground floor of the *Daily Worker* building, the
temperature was in the mid nineties. While his temporary contact

made the inevitable phone call, he stared with lusterless turtle eyes at the books of William Z. Foster, Howard Fast, and Jack London, and wished it were not quite so hot. Then he might have been able to carry a small box of chocolate turtles in his coat pocket without having them lapse into a viscous brown pool. The temporary contact did not take long. Whoever it was she had talked to had evidently been very impressed with Mr. Tikjan's piece of intelligence. She instructed Mr. Tikjan to return to Washington that evening, to draw on a new and more lavish expense account, to inform the Washington contact, who would re-establish touch with him at once, that he was operating under special credentials — documentary evidence of this would reach the contact in question during the current week — and, from this point on, never to lose touch with Dr. Gottfried Krehan, who had now become his sole reason for existing. On leaving the *Daily Worker* building, Mr. Tikjan should by no means go straight to the station. He should, instead, take the subway to Macy's, and, once there, stroll purposefully to the toy department where, as evidence of his intentions as a serious shopper, he was empowered to buy toys costing no less than five, no more than ten dollars.

Mr. Tikjan, an adept in the standard devices of shadowing and being shadowed, followed instructions to the letter. Once at Macy's he discovered a new dimension. To his vast surprise, he found that selecting the requisite toy produced in him a quite unanalyzable pleasure. A three-inch tall royal mouse pair, King and Queen, in crowns, fluted Elizabethan ruffs, red coronation capes, and sitting together on a mouse throne, with a murine Stone of Scone beneath them — the throne was two dollars extra and, he thought, distinctly worth it — came within his budget. He was just about to take the mice when two toy neighbors of theirs captivated his eye to the extent that Mr. Tikjan unexpectedly discovered himself perpetrating the first joke of his drab life. These neighbors were a pair of turtle Apaches — Montmartre variety — of green velveteen and felt. The male Apache had a red casquette on the side of his head and a cigarette dangling from rakish reptile lips. The female's hat was a single full-blown rose. As Mr. Tikjan paid for the droll creatures, he already visualized them perched like totems at either end of the mantel in his boardinghouse bedroom, an opened box of chocolate turtles between them. He wondered what his landlady, Mrs. Herring, would make of this newly acquired taste in frou-frou decoration.

On his way to the station, Mr. Tikjan, gift-wrapped modernistic turtles tucked under one arm, used the accepted routine methods to rid himself of possible shadowers. Before leaving Macy's, he changed elevators twice, finally shifting to an escalator which carried him to the basement and then up to the first floor again. He took the subway instead of a taxi — in a taxi there was no particular protection against the "forward pass" technique, in accordance with which maneuver the first shadower, whom one thinks one is shaking off, passes the ball to a second and even a third car. He changed subways no less than three times. He quadrangulated himself, as it were, on street corners where there were four stoplights, reversing his field so that he would be able to notice if any person passed him in transit more than once.

Next morning Mr. Tikjan found himself in a mood of pleasurable anticipation. He felt it would turn out to be a good day. It did. His new contact — Mr. Tikjan had thought, at the time, that the *Daily Worker* temporary contact was imprecise in her use of the verb, "re-establish" — proved to be more amiable than the preceding one. And he had come back on duty just in the nick of time to catch his quarry breaking trail. That afternoon Dr. Krehan bought a round-trip railroad ticket for South Bend, Indiana. And that evening, for the first time in his life, Mr. Tikjan occupied an air-cooled roomette on a train bound in the general direction of Chicago.

The roomette was directly in front of the one assigned to Dr. Krehan. It crossed the mind of Dr. Krehan, who in his childhood had been devoted to the *Arabian Nights*, that the little dark man in the roomette next to his would be well cast as a villainous vizier in some such tale as that of *Aladdin* or that of *Noureddin Ali and the Damsel Enis El Jelis*. He also wondered where he had seen him before. Then he forgot all about him. Mr. Tikjan, though, did not forget about Dr. Krehan. Each time he casually passed by the Krehan roomette door, the quarry was writing. When, around ten o'clock, Dr. Krehan walked back to the observation platform for his usual evening constitutional, he left his roomette door ajar. Mr. Tikjan waited exactly two minutes by the cheap watch on his wrist, then darted in. In case Dr. Krehan should return before he had finished what he had to do, Mr. Tikjan had an alibi all ready. It was to the effect that he had missed his proper door and mistaken Dr. Krehan's roomette for his own. It was not necessary to use the alibi. Dr. Krehan did not come back for twenty minutes. Before five were over, Mr. Tikjan, who worked fast and deftly, had taken care of what he had come to do.

It was absurdly easy. Dr. Krehan had been writing letters. The envelopes, unsealed, lay on the portable writing desk furnished by the Pullman porter. Beside them were several sheets of correspondence signed and ready to insert. Sighting his saboteur's miniature camera, Mr. Tikjan quickly made four exposures. The camera, the size of a cigarette lighter, was a very nice piece of goods which had once belonged to no less a personage than Reichsmarschall Goering. It had been lying on a dressing table in the main bedroom of Goering's villa near Berchtesgaden when the second armored division of the French First Army, with Mr. Tikjan, who was nothing if not versatile, accredited to them as an English and German speaking interpreter, entered the mountain retreat. Laughing and singing, the French troops had knocked off the gold-foil necks of case after case of excellent champagne. The prudent Mr. Tikjan had confined his looting to a pound box of chocolate windmills from Holland and the diminutive camera.

It was not very difficult to follow Dr. Krehan next day, though it must be admitted that Mr. Tikjan found academic processions and convocations excessively tedious. He drowsed a little while the speaker of the day, a former United States ambassador to Russia, warned the audience against the dangers of excess in anti-Soviet reaction.

"I tremble," said Mr. Kennan in measured tones, "when I see this attempt to make a semi-religious cult out of emotional-political currents of the moment, and particularly when I note that these currents are ones exclusively negative in nature, designed to appeal only to men's capacity for hatred and fear, never to their capacity for forgiveness and charity and understanding."

It was hot in the new Notre Dame Fine Arts Building where the convocation was being held. Mr. Tikjan nodded. He did not know it, but he had seen Mr. Kennan before — or, at least, an unreasonable simulacrum of him caricatured as a capitalist-reactionary-bandit-saboteur in the temperate pages of *Krokodil*. To be entirely fair to Mr. Tikjan, the former ambassador to Russia did look a bit different in an academic gown. Also, he was not carrying a bloody dagger in his teeth as he had done in the pages of *Krokodil*.

Dr. Krehan had lunch with the dignitaries in the Morris Inn. Mr. Tikjan waited patiently outside. Dr. Krehan was escorted on a formal and lengthy tour of the campus. Mr. Tikjan followed in his train. Dr. Krehan inspected the famous old church on the campus. Mr. Tikjan stared dolefully at the golden points made by the candles before the altar in the Lady Chapel. Dr. Krehan had dinner with the dignitaries in the Morris Inn. Mr. Tikjan waited patiently outside again.

The Indiana air was still soft and clear and delicate with spring; the wilting nights were still some weeks off. The new grass was sweet smelling in the dusk. As the twilight drew on, the gold dome of the University lit up. Fireflies gleamed off and on, on and off, against the dark green of the shrubbery and in the darkening air between him and the dome. Mr. Tikjan noted them dully. The fitful flashing of the little insect lanterns made him think of the glimmering candles before the Lady altar. It was just as weak, just as picturesque, just as anachronistic. It did not occur to Mr. Tikjan that the star shine, just then pricking through the luminous blue envelope overhead, was equally slight, equally fitful, and, according to the tenets of Einsteinean relativity, no more fixed. In fact, had Mr. Tikjan only been interested, the Department of Astronomy could have informed him that the firefly light corresponded exactly to the illumination, filtering down to man through untold millions of miles of space and countless light years of time, from the first magnitude star, Canopus. Candle power, on the other hand, was fifty times greater than both star and firefly light. All things, in other words, were relative. But Mr. Tikjan, nursing the cold light of his own little absolute, would probably have been uninterested in such figures.

At midnight Dr. Krehan took a taxi to the somnolent little station that only really came alive in football season. Mr. Tikjan followed. Next afternoon he developed his film back in Washington, the toy turtles beadily looking on. The name on one of the envelopes was

Desmond. The accompanying letter indicated that Dr. Krehan meditated visiting his old friend, John Desmond, sometime in September. Or else in early October.

Mr. Tikjan scratched his head meditatively. Here was news indeed. The Desmond dossier was growing more important.

That was the way Mr. Tikjan spent his May and June. The Desmonds spent theirs with flowers.

The only trouble with leaving the house on Hurst Monceux and moving to the beach house was leaving the flowers. And this had been such a spring for growing things! Even Professor Desmond, who used to say that he had ten thumbs — and that not one of them was green — could see that.

This spring, he thought to himself, was Malorian: Guinevere and her ladies in waiting in green dresses, riding on palfreys in pageant procession, through a springtide May of Malory. It was bright with the thin, far trumpets of Debussy's *Les Fêtes* blowing the chase across sun-dappled glades.

Even the tulips and the pansies were exciting, if one bothered to look closely at their common but exquisite selves. Tulips brought Holland into his yard, right up to the warm red brick of his espaliered garage. Tulips were red-faced burgess wives, Rubens rouged, primly bedizened vrouw out of Vermeer. As the wind passed over their orderly, gossiping rows, they nodded yellow Batavian turbans in the coolth of the air and the spilth of the sun, while, at their green-clocked feet, the fat-cheeked Persian-kitten faces of pansies lapped up, like milk, the longhosed trickling coolness of the nozzle Toby let drip into their black-loamed trench.

The Wheeler boy went up and down the grass swales with his power mower. Moira laid aside her Pyle's *Robin Hood* and, chin propped on the grass, watched him. It was nice to get so close to the new grass before it was mowed. The blades seemed so tall and straight on eye level. It was like being in Sherwood Forest. As the breeze rippled them, the blades all bent one way, like forest men hunting low in Lincoln green. The breeze grew stronger. It was a real wind now — a sheriff wind, pursed, insolent. As the sheriff wind swept by on its charger — it grew darker now, and Moira thought the charger must be black — the grass turned from green to silver. Each grass man seemed to be baring his blade's grey-silver sheen. There was rain coming. You could smell it soft on the air.

It was only a sunshower at first. It made Mother think of babies. Of Kristin, as she had been some years back. Of the new baby, as she — or he — would be by next spring. Under the wind-and-sun-and-water of the shower it was as if baby clouds raced, shouting, in their worsted rainbow sunsuits through all the sprinklers on the lawns of heaven.

From Professor Desmond's study window, Karen tried to catch the gold of forsythia in paint from her palette. Today, anyway, it was impossible. Suddenly pensive, she put down the brush, thinking, for the first time in months, of the masquer Viking at Jack's Halloween party. Maybe underneath, though, she'd really been thinking of him all afternoon, for, when it was done, she had intended calling her picture *Saga of Forsythia*. There was something breathless and breathtaking about these aureate bushes that overnight had blossomed in glorious gold, yellow-mailed and helmed like jarls, sun-haired like Vikings breaking at a run from Thorfinn's dragon ship. But today she couldn't quite catch their essential quality. Karen sighed.

There was more than a sunshower in the offing now. The study grew darker. A few heavy drops plopped into the bushes that fringed the screened window. Then the rain came down like silver lances massed to charge. It drummed on the slate roof overhead till the sloping planes of gray-blue pigeon color were one flowing sheet of water. It pocked the pavement and made the blacktop driveway steam. Then, as suddenly as it began, it was all over, except for a dripping from the evergreens. There were no casualties, if one did not count the magnolia petals that were down on the lawn.

Professor Desmond could not help a single pang, however. Magnolias were his favorite flower. Looking at their old rose and silver huddled pell-mell against the rain-dark grass, he had a sudden Viking image all his own. He had watched the delicate petals spring and bridle under the shower, like swan maidens bathing in a mere, like the chatelaines of his garden slaking spring heat in the rain. Now they had fled like Valkyries before the darkling onset of the Viking wind, dropping their white plumage in terror, leaving the tree a glistening thorn bush, dispossessed, disenchanted. With a smile Professor Desmond turned from the streaming upstairs windowpane. What would Toby think of thoughts like this at his age?

Kristin was at his knee, *Jonathan and the Rainbow* in her hand. "Daddy," she said, "where is our rainbow?"

Where, indeed? One really ought to domesticate rainbows as well as Siamese cats.

"We haven't got one," he said. "We have no leprechauns, either. And no pots of gold."

Then a thought struck him.

"Come out back a minute, Kris," he said. "Maybe we have got a rainbow at that."

He had spilled some motor oil that morning in front of the garage door. It lay now, an iridescent splotch, on the wet blacktop.

"There's your rainbow, Kris," he said, pointing to it.

The child seemed satisfied. She squatted over the opalescence, crooning to herself.

The small change of everyday family experience made its slow way, day by day, into the pockets of Professor Desmond's imagination. It never seemed much at any given time, but, pausing to take stock every now and then, he found that it was rapidly totting up to a good round sum on the credit side of the Human Comedy's great ledger. With children in the house, *la condition humaine* had a way of turning from an existentialist trap into a two-reel comedy of the old Mack Sennett variety, complete with greased slides, booby traps, crazy tongs, mad chases, and Keystone Cops. Children were better than a novel. The critics always blethered about life. Children were living. One lived to learn that nursery rhymes were the higher wisdom — including the inexorable one about the horrors of arithmetic. With all the good will in the world, it was hard for a professor to get round the economic facts of life.

Returning to summer was a little like making a dowsing rod work. You either could or you couldn't. The Desmond family happened to be a family that could. It settled down to the serious business of loafing and inviting its soul with all the leisurely and practiced excitement a real dowser brings to his profession. All during May and the first three weeks in June, their legs were twitching on the city pavements like the forked stick of a dowser when it smells sweet water. Now that school was out, the peeled wand of the summer turned in their hands like a live thing. They'd struck two months — and a bit over — of free-running time, as pure and clear as any free-running spring that was ever dowsed. It was a freehand display of that virtually lost and most liberal art of all, the art of sheer living.

Summer was good for Professor Desmond's business, too. He kept his office under his hat. One just had to sit back and let the ideas flow into the drowsy mind like so many slow-moving summer clouds. They were mostly essay ideas, vagrant thoughts that came and went like random eddies of air. Sweet-swinked Summer was herself an essay mood annihilating the lazing personality to Andrew Marvell's green thought in a green shade. It was a time for fireflies' green intimations in the greener grass; for sleepy seagull images that were not quite poetry but on the verge of poetry.

Sometimes a summer image would particularize itself more sharply. It happened under July sunsets. The sky would burn as red as the face of a big-top barker hawking his toys; the translucent water would turn green as a bird on a carnival stick. In a sand bar pool, black minnows would flick slimpsy tails in ballet formation, each supple sibling swimming effortlessly in his little crimson sky, slickly darting from one end of the pool to the other. On nights like these, so still one could hear the voices of girls and boys a mile away over the clear water, the stars pricked out a carrousel light and the huntress moon became instead a Chinese goddess breathing peace and serenity and the amplitude of love.

And there were bracing northern days as well as lotus-eating southern ones. Days that started with the smell of coffee and bacon even sharper than usual in the nostrils. The sun would shine and the breeze blow off the lake, trapping the gold of sunshine and the lavender of air in the pajamas that flapped on the backyard line. Before noon, though, the land breeze would be a little more than just stiff. Then out would come sweaters and Mackinaw. Apple logs would be kindled in the fireplace. In the yard close to the house Professor Desmond would grill fat bubbling patties of Canadian beef on aluminum foil that kept the flavor in and the flame out. He would open a bottle of Black Horse cream porter and another one of ale for himself and Mother, blend those two honest creatures of malt into the single black velvet consistency that was jocularly but libelously known as 'arf-and-'arf — like the soul, it was actually a divine unity — and pour it into the glass tankards which, before their transformation into drinking beakers, had been peanut butter jars. There would be English ginger beer in stone bottles for the children. Then the family would top off their back porch meal with blueberries shipped down from Muskoka, round as little basket balls, frosted grape-blue, and submerged in thick cream.

Fireworks were illegal in New York State, but not in the Province of Ontario, a fact which gratified Father, if not Mother. So the Desmonds were — within limits — able to celebrate a good old-fashioned Fourth. "Within limits" meant lady crackers instead of cannon crackers, cokes instead of lemonade, ice cream in packages instead of out of a home freezer that always left a salty taste in the resultant product, portable radios on the beach instead of gramophones on the verandah. The essence of the Fourth remained the same. Thunder growled toward the end of the afternoon. Then the skies cleared again. The evening seemed twice as long as any other evening, which made it a very long evening indeed, since, to start with, July evenings were already half as long again as those of other months. As darkness drew on at last and the sand cooled underfoot, every headland between Buffalo and Port Colborne, on the Canadian side of the lake, and, on the American side, between Dunkirk and Buffalo, broke into dancing fire, into a Mendelssohn scherzo of sparklers in children's hands.

As usual, the skyrockets were the best. So trite, yet so spectacular, such evanescent secular Christmas trees, thought Professor Desmond, as he touched his punk to a rocket on its inclined wooden runway, and still another fire drake whooshed aloft in a scatter of red and green balls. The golden serpentine, in its swift passage, made a soft radiant trail over the mirroring water, momentarily lighting up the shadows of motor boats hoisted high in their steel slings just off shore. Because of the water reflector, the fire arc seemed to last longer before it hissed to extinction beneath the darkness of Lake

Erie. Another went up with a soft explosion like a bag of old
silk ripping. Then another. Then another. "A-a-a-h!" murmured the
children, grouped on the wall. And everything was over for another
year.

When, sated with soft drinks and spectacle, the children had
gone to bed, and the murmurous dark was quiet once again except
for the whispering of the poplar leaves and the waves' susurrus,
Professor Desmond, flashlight in hand, walked over his little patch
of beach to make sure nothing had been left smoldering. He kicked
aside a guttered pinwheel and several charred rocket sticks. Sparkler
wires lay cold and bent on the sand. A mist was moving in from
the lake. Professor Desmond had a moment of unease. How stood
it with Liberty's torch? he asked himself. Was it, too, going out
in the night? Did the democratic *mystique* begin to flicker fitfully?
If so, it must be for want of knowing what it meant. It meant
something all right. Secularly speaking, the democratic idea was still
the world's last, best hope of earth. A final rocket went up many
headlands away, to the sound of muffled explosions. Its red and
green Very light traced a delicate pattern on the night. They were
finishing off the display at the Cherry Hill Club. Professor Desmond
remembered his Memorial Day decision to drive the children to
Washington come August.

Professor Desmond welcomed one caesural pause in the Summer's
hexameter movement. Once every year he took the children to
the Canadian amusement park, ten miles from Crescent Beach,
that was appropriately and conventionally named Crystal Beach.
If the truth were only known, he went a most willing martyr, on
these annual jaunts, even as Mrs. Desmond went an unwilling one.
Some unanalyzable, seedy, but potent magic attracted him in amusement parks. He was drawn to the arcades, the shooting galleries
with their bloodless carnage, the distorting mirrors, the carrousels.
Most especially to the carrousels. He thought the merry-go-round
one of man's more felicitous inventions.

So, apparently, did Kristin. Mounted on a snow-white unicorn
that rose and fell on its bright brass pole, the child flashed by
her father for a third successive ride. Her lips were parted and her
red hair streamed on the wind. For a while, she was dream-borne,

myth-borne, music-borne. For a space, she satisfied primordial desires in him as well as in herself. After her came the splendid steeds, red-nostriled, rampant forever, and the heraldic beasts: the blue stags and red lions and green leopards. Kristin, intent on her fairy tale ride, did not wave to him as she cantered stately past. Nor he to her. He remembered the rules of the game from his own far childhood. He knew it would break the spell that, even to childhood, came only once and was as fragile as crystal. Instead, he leaned back against the hard green wooden bench and broke out a fresh pack of cigarettes.

Cutting across the hot picnic grove afterward, on their way back to the parking lot, replete with waffles and ice cream bars, and a little tipsy afoot after a last jolting visit to the newest fun house, they passed the striped pavilions of the fortunetellers. Unexpectedly Karen stopped.

"Dad," she said. "Can you wait another minute? I want my fortune told."

Professor Desmond could be very arbitrary when he chose.

"No," he said. "I don't approve of fortunetellers. I don't think they're healthy."

Karen pouted.

"I'll use my own money," she said.

"That's not the point," he said firmly.

"All the girls get their fortunes told. Great-aunt Dorothy tells fortunes."

"Not for money," said Professor Desmond. "Besides, I can't do anything about Great-aunt Dorothy. If she wants to tell your fortune, O.K. But you stick to Great-aunt Dorothy's tea leaves."

"Sister Albinus," said Sheila helpfully, "told us that she went to a man fortuneteller to see if she should enter the convent. He said she was going on a long journey, so she entered the convent."

"Damn it!" said Professor Desmond, exasperated. "What have Sister Albinus' spiritual decisions to do with my disapproving of Karen's going to fortunetellers?"

Karen looked indignantly at her mother.

"John, dear," said Mother. "I can't see that it could do much harm."

When she smiled, her dimple showed.

"John," she said, when he made no answer, "remember Karen was born with a caul."

"So was David Copperfield," he said sullenly. "So was Sigmund Freud. So what?"

As was customary, when the women of his household formed a solid phalanx, Professor Desmond gave in. This time he gave in with very bad grace. To say that he did not approve of fortune-tellers was putting it mildly. He was against tampering with the Fates in any form. As a rationalist, he did not think it could be done. As an Irishman, he feared the worst could eventuate from even trying to do it. From no point of view was he prepared to be an appanage of the Witch of Endor's ancient church — historically, he supposed, it was almost the most ancient and worst church of all — which, in one shape or another, comprised so many more members nowadays even than it used to. It was a strange thing, when one came to think of it, he said to himself, this startling rise of age-old necromancy in what called itself a modern and plumed itself on being a skeptical world. Thomas called Didymus was not prepared to believe in the risen Saviour till he had put his mortal fingers into the dint of the lance and the print of the nails. Thomas' diddling *didymi* of descendants went him one better. Before they would believe, they demanded spirit stuff to touch and pull like taffy candy. Well, he was not having any of it. Professor Desmond lit another cigarette and went on fuming.

The burnt offering of Toby's timid but decisive plucking at his sleeve did not appease him. He had never precisely suffered fools gladly. And, in his book, these were the worst fools of all, these greasy, asthmatic, horrible old women, these tarnished sybils, these backstairs fates, sitting inside hot tents in summer amusement parks; shuffling decks of cards that were bloated and thickened like themselves with age; waiting, before crystal balls, at the beck and call of that tyrannous, sinister plaything, the *planchette*; messing about with dreary *tables tournants*, behind the swishing bead drapes of cold winter rooms. And the messages that came through from their Iroquois controls! Were those astral Amerindians all imbeciles? Angrily, he stubbed out his half-smoked cigarette.

The pavilion flap parted and Karen came out, white-faced.

"Dad!" she called. "Come here at once. There's something wrong with the fortuneteller."

Professor Desmond rushed into the tent. The woman, glassy-eyed, light flecks of foam on her otherwise dry lips, sat rigidly erect, as if in a cataleptic trance. She was speaking in a hoarse grating voice. He listened and, to his complete surprise, realized that he could understand her, though she spoke not English, but old Viking of the period of the *Poetic Edda.*

"*Eptir dauða Brynhildar,*" said the fortuneteller, speaking by rote, as if she were repeating from dictation, "*vóro gǫr bál tvau, annat Sigurði, ok brann ðat fyrr, en Brynhildr var á oðro brend, ok var hon í reið. Svá er sagt, at Brynhildr ók með reiðinni á helveg ok fór . . .*"

Professor Desmond said the strange words over to himself in English:

"*After the death of Brynhild were two bale-fires made, one for Sigurth, and that pyre blazed, and Brynhild was burned on the other, and she was laid in a chariot. Now the story is told that Brynhild drove in the chariot on Hell Way, and she fared . . .*"

There was a curious choking sound in the fortuneteller's throat. Professor Desmond took her wrists and chafed them. He felt a fool doing it. But he had read somewhere that, in cases like this, it could do some good.

"Here, now," he said. "This won't do at all, you know."

The sound of the unfamiliar voice seemed to bring the woman out of her trance seizure. She blinked once or twice. Her eyes became more normal. She turned to the man across the table from her.

"Why did you break the rapport?" she asked him harshly.

Professor Desmond ignored the question for one of his own.

"*Kan De snakke Norsk?*" he asked her. "*Eller Dansk? Eller Svensk?* Do you speak any Scandinavian? Icelandic, perhaps?"

She shook her head.

"No," she said tonelessly.

Then, in a more lifelike tone:

"How very odd! I have never had such clear contact before. There were two Indians beside me, and a bearded man in a helmet. They belonged to very old times, all three of them. One of the Indians was a woman. A girl, almost. Where is the girl whose palm I was reading?"

Professor Desmond cleared his throat.

"I am the child's father," he said stiffly. "May I pay you now?"

The fortuneteller shook her head emphatically.

"I will take no money," she said. "It was because of the girl I made the contact. I know it. I can tell. I should like to finish the reading for her. There will be no fee."

This time it was Professor Desmond who did the head shaking. And just as emphatically.

"I do not think it would be advisable," he said formally.

The fortuneteller looked closely at him. She shrugged her shoulders.

"You are her father?" she said. "I will tell your fortune then."

"No, thank you," he said, rising.

"With the Tarots," she said, wheedling him, riffling an ornate old deck before him on the table. "I do not do it often with the Tarots. They are very precious and very wise."

Despite himself, Professor Desmond was tempted. He had often wanted to scrutinize a real Tarot deck. But he shook his head again.

The woman did not seem to heed his refusal. She held out a card toward him. On it was a man with a sword.

"Look. On the *tarocchi*," she said. "The man with the sword."

"No, thank you," he said firmly, and a little regretfully.

On the ride back to Crescent Beach, Mother and Karen kept very quiet. They knew that the man in their household was pleasant enough — even biddable — but that he was not above the I-told-you-so kind of thing. But this time Professor Desmond did not reproach the two elder members of his harem. He was thinking of other things. He was morally convinced that the fortuneteller had spoken the truth when she said she knew no Scandinavian. Yet, when he first came into the tent, she had been speaking the fourteenth-century tongue of the old Eddas. No, that queer performance of hers had been no hoax. But, in that case, had it not been even more alarming than a hoax? He could not shake off for days the eerie imprint the incident had made on him.

ᴧᴧ

Oh Say Can You See?

THE Desmonds, four strong, Mother, Father, Moira, and Sheila — Karen stayed home to keep house for Kristin, Rajah, Ranee, Sillerton Jackson, and Grandmother and Grandfather Hansen — rolled down to their cousins' home in Silver Springs, just over the Maryland border from Washington, in ten minutes short of twelve hours which, thought Professor Desmond, when you allowed for a lunch stop in the Pennsylvania State Forest and a tour of Gettysburg, was not bad time at all. Things went well all the way. The real intention of the trip, on his part, was to forge for the children, on the good old-fashioned anvil of historic association, an emotional atmosphere of civic romance and political mystique in the old high sense of the word political. That is: the things pertaining to the City, in this case the City of Man which was builded on that other goodly City, the City of God.

Running swiftly through the Alleghenies, the four of them caught fleeting glimpses of the American beasts who had belonged to the land long before the coming of the red man even, and who belonged to it still: a dappled fawn with its mother; a coon, black-masked, one near-human paw upraised; an otter fishing in a mountain stream. Fold upon fold, gap upon gap of rolling undulant hills, their long flanks heavy with the fell of soft-timbered forests, opened sweetly outward into the blue distance. Once, from the crest of a rise, they saw a butter-yellow house — of the palest butter color, though — a

red church opposite, and, alongside the church, a scatter of tomb-
stones in a toy graveyard. That was America as Professor Desmond
had known it in his youth, and as his children, through the power
of sympathetic identification, could still get to know it. Almost
every farmhouse in the Pennsylvania countryside was crowned by
Calder mobiles of television aerials, many of them as box-kite
elaborate as some museum prototype of the Wrights' *Kittyhawk*.
That was part of the new America, and, when all was said and done,
just as picturesque as anything in the old. One would be nostalgic
for these memories some day.

Once, passing an Elementary Public School on Route 350, near
Tyrone, Professor Desmond saw, through a window, a furled flag
leaning against a blackboard, waiting the return of the children.
Patriotism, it was true, could deteriorate into a scoundrel's last
refuge. It was also the cradle of civic virtue and the honorable pall
of the hero. That furled flag, waiting in the empty, varnished, sun-
flecked classroom, was America, too. So were the ribald, salty signs
chalked up on the backs of the great gear-groaning, toiling trucks
he passed on the down grades. *Watch my rear, not hers,* said one.
It was good moral advice with a frontiersman's humorous quirky
bite in it. Another read: *Martians, go home!* There was something
indigenously, cosmically American in that tall-tale brashness. Then
he remembered that, in certain European capitals at that very
moment, cold, steely-eyed men with no laughter in their hearts,
men who knew what they were about every second, were busy
writing on walls and hustings: *Amis, go home!*

But they couldn't go home, not just yet. The sentry-go had
been thrust upon them. They dared not abdicate.

His hands loose on the steering wheel, Professor Desmond said
over to himself the close of John Dryden's great *Secular Masque:*

> All, all of a piece throughout:
> Thy chase had a beast in view;
> Thy wars brought nothing about;
> Thy lovers were all untrue.
> 'Tis well an old age is out,
> And time to begin a new.

No, it was not time to go home just yet.

There was a perceptible change in the climate of the mind when they got close to the Mason-Dixon line. Soft vocables rolled not in black voices alone. Not only Southern courtesy but the warmer sun of the old South was in the voice of the white toll-taker on the bridge over the Susquehanna.

"Take Route 15 straight into Gettysburg," he said in reply to Professor Desmond's question. The softness was welcome to their Northern ears.

Above all, was Gettysburg America. Here, if anywhere in America, was sacred ground. Here in these woods and fields. Here on this *haute* and haunted field of Gettysburg were ghosts, and no man made these fields his home. Professor Desmond's scalp prickled. His hackles lifted. He wondered if the children felt the presences as he did. Toby did, certainly. She fell very quiet while their car moved in and out of the patches of dark silent woodland and through the sun-drenched glades; while they drove past Little Round Top's masked gun batteries, where so many of the brave had fallen. The shadows were beginning to lengthen. It was the time of bird song. But no birds sang on the quiet field of the slain.

Dark, those woods. Dark, too, those sun-drenched glades. Dark the hardwoods in the late light. Dark the oaks and locusts. Dark the beeches and clean maples. Dark the mortuary bronze; dark the end of all the bloody travail; dark the memory thereof. There was memorial statuary everywhere: silent metal people and people of mute stone. The plunging bronzes — outstretched hand and hat, and caracoling hoof — held sway, exerted authority still, controlled man's destinies for weal or woe.

Quiet, without comment, they drove out of the field of Gettysburg and on to the Washington road. The long evening light held on the hills. That Arabian enchanter, the sky, laid his dark cloud rug across the slopes, then snapped it back again to disclose other and still more glorious vistas.

"Look!" said Professor Desmond, pointing.

"Oh, yes," said Moira, bestowing on the end of that long day her ultimate accolade. "This is better than Wald's farm, and almost as good as every Christmas."

Sheila was tired of scenery. The only thing she never tired of, it seemed, was people. And chatter.

"How many miles have we come today?" she asked.

Professor Desmond consulted the speedometer.

"Three hundred and ninety so far," he said.

"I don't see things getting rounder," said Sheila.

"You don't see what?" asked Professor Desmond.

"Things getting rounder," said Sheila. "They told us in third grade that the earth was round."

"It is," said Professor Desmond. "Only it's so large that the curving is gradual. So you can't see it except on the horizon. Or up in the stratosphere."

"What's the stratosphere?" asked Sheila.

"Never mind now," said Professor Desmond, as usual, tiring of the discussion. He was at the stage summer motorists reach of being drunk with sun and road and mileage.

The arbitrary cloture was all right with Sheila, who was, at bottom, a complete relativist.

"O.K.," she said brightly. "They say different things in different grades, anyway. In third grade they said the earth was perfectly round. Now they say it's flat on the ends."

Looking in the rear mirror at his daughter with the gamine's face, Professor Desmond refrained from retort. He knew he was reputed a good teacher. But he had never yet been able to explain anything whatsoever to these four girl children of his.

"Skip it, Sheila," was all he said, as he settled back against the cushion for the final thirty mile stretch of road.

Mother, sitting beside him on the front seat, laughed a little to herself.

"Dad," said Moira in a drowsy voice. "If you died and we were grown up, could Mother enter a convent?"

Professor Desmond did not care for purely hypothetical questions. He did not like to speculate on his own demise, either.

"I suppose there'd be no obstacle, canonically speaking," he said in a somewhat chilly tone. "But I rather think she wouldn't."

Sitting beside her husband, Mother smiled her secret smile. She gave his arm a little squeeze and felt him relax against the back rest.

"Light me a cigarette, will you, Toby?" he asked her.

They came into Silver Springs a little after dark. Sprinklers played over the lawns. There was a tinkle of ice in glasses on shadowed screened porches. Cigars glowed in and out like fireflies. There were low-pitched bursts of laughter here and there along the streets. One could smell the wet grass and the water from the hoses in the hands of suburban Tritons forgetting, in this aqueous way, the heat and dust of the day. Mrs. Desmond's Washington cousins made them welcome with the casual opulence Professor Desmond always associated with his wife's relations.

Professor Desmond had not been in Washington in more than sixteen years. Despite its mushroom growth over that period, he found the city more beautiful and more intimate than ever.

He approved of the new buildings; of the Atomic Energy Commission; of the Federal Reserve. Of the new apartments, like the Woodson, all shining stone and glass. Of the fountains spilling dark green water before the gleaming white façades. The State Department building still looked grayly antediluvian — as it should. One had more confidence in it that way. The New Corcoran already looked old. The Mall had always reminded him of Paris. It still did, after sixteen years. Across the Basin from the Jefferson Memorial, the Bureau of Standards, a steel-etched Louvre, blended into the August heat haze. Only the locusts' brazen stridency, bronzing the hot afternoon, was the same as the last time he had been there. All day and night the stridulating insects were busy, sucking sap out of sound tree limbs, like the noisy despoilers in the Kremlin.

At noon the next day Mrs. Desmond and the two girls lunched, in chaste but regal splendor, at the *Cosmos Club* on Grandfather Hansen's card. The new building at 2121 Massachusetts Avenue was more palatial and more up to date than the old one had been. Mrs. Desmond decided she preferred the comparative mustiness of the old one. Coming out after lunch into the white blazing sunlight that fountained down from a cloudless sky, Sheila, who loved chocolate turtles, tugged at her mother's sleeve and whispered something in her ear about the dark-complexioned, fleshy-beaked little man standing by the letter box. Mrs. Desmond stared at him a trifle absently at first. Why, the child was right, she said to herself.

The man did look markedly like a chocolate turtle. If she had happened to notice him independently, she might have called him a parrot or toucan. But chocolate turtle was definitely better.

Despite Sheila's blandishments, Mother remained adamant. It was much too hot for chocolate turtles. They would visit the Franciscan Catacombs, which were sure to be cool, and after them the Mellon Gallery. The Catacombs were not nearly so impressive as she remembered them from her childhood. In fact, they struck her now as having a distinctly Tunnel-of-Loveish air. The children seemed satisfied, though, so that was all that mattered.

Walking through the Mellon Gallery for the first time, Mother, who usually did not care for Henry James, recalled his description of the *Galerie d'Appolon's* "charged, coloured and confounding air." How perfect an impression it was of the way in which a great art gallery's massed color smote upon the mind's eye and ear! Mrs. Desmond dutifully collected reproductions of Rouault, Dufy, and Utrillo. At the same time, it seemed to her, a great deal of what passed for contemporary art suffered from one kind of fetishism or another when it should have suffered from love. The Muses, draped or undraped, did not dance so gracefully as in the days when they still had both left and right feet. Catch Renoir — or even Degas — painting their nudes, as Morris Hirshfield did, with two left feet! They had too much integration and too much downright good sense for such fantods as that.

So had an earlier Frenchman, Rouget by name, before whose *Le peintre David par son élève, Rouget,* Mrs. Desmond paused spellbound. What fire! What authority! What vigor! What arrogance! What a living monument of the human spirit! Above all — as Hugo and Saint Beuve would have said — *quel race!* Where was it nowadays?

Oddly enough, that evening Professor Desmond asked himself the same question in other terms, and came up with a slightly different answer. Usually it was he who was the pessimist, and Toby who was the optimist. This time they exchanged parts. Not all the way, however.

Standing in the great secular temple of the Lincoln Memorial, where everything was cool and hushed and where, despite the cathedral quiet, every footstep, every whisper became magnified until it seemed as if the whole nation must be there speaking low, Professor Desmond looked up and read, graven on the wall like votive tablets to justice, charity, and mercy, the great sounding organ words of the *Gettysburg* oration and of the *Second Inaugural Address.* The grave music rang, pianissimo, in his head. Here, he said to himself, was the climax of all political wisdom: power tamed and forebearing. Here was the exception that proved Lord Acton's rule that power corrupted; and made a tinkling cymbal of Count Oxenstierna's dreary dictum that man is governed without wisdom.

The people all around him felt it as much as he did. He had noted, in the Union Station, that the book kiosks were still selling that specimen of water-closet journalism, *Washington Confidential.* Here was a truer sort of Washington confidential, these tourist pilgrims from every state in the Union in their slacks, sport shirts, huaraches; their cameras aimed, despite the failing light; their faces intent in silent consecration.

Professor Desmond looked up at the words of the *Gettysburg Address. Now we are engaged in a great civil war* . . . It was so again, only now the civil war that divided the hearts and souls of men was a civil war fought with new weapons — with daggers of the mind and poisoned vials of idea — over all the lands and seas and airways of the entire globe. The issues were again the same: slavery versus freedom; old fate against free will. *The world will little note, nor long remember, what we say here* . . . But it had noted, it had remembered. So long as liberty endured, it would continue to remember. *It is for the living, rather, to be dedicated here to the unfinished work which they who fought here have thus far so nobly advanced.* That kind of work was never finished. It never would be finished, so long as man was man. So long as the forces of light contended against the forces of darkness. Professor Desmond remembered the tremendous gesture, at the end of the *Chanson de Roland,* when Charlemagne, the old champion of Christendom, heard that a new war had broken out on the marches of his kingdom. And he tore his long white beard and wept even as Abraham Lincoln had wept in the long night watches of his war. *Ci falt la geste,* said the old chronicler of the *Chanson.* Here ends this Geste. Not: Here ends the war. The war never ends. And it is all the same war.

When Professor Desmond finally shepherded the children out

of the Memorial, lights were just coming on in the summer-scented, echoing dusk. A lighted plane, flying very low, passed noiselessly overhead in the moth-soft evening light. The greatest of the evening lamps of Washington was the soft radiance of the lighted Capitol, tiered like a wedding cake of the Republic, behind dark clumps of trees as formally and precisely grouped as in a Grant Wood painting. A sickle moon was just rising over the Memorial.

It was growing late now, but he thought they might just have time enough to squeeze in the Jefferson Memorial on the south shore of the tidal basin. Standing on the steps of the Lincoln Memorial, Professor Desmond looked across at the Washington Monument from whose top the children had that afternoon surveyed the city on the Potomac. The tall obelisk cast a long white shadow down the Reflecting Pool, companioned by the short white reflection of a toy sailboat becalmed on the evening-blue mirror surface. It was, he thought, like a pier glass from the Versailles of Rochambeau's day affectionately preserving the minuet grace of an age of powdered wigs and silken breeches; an age, moreover, which was not, here in America, a symbol of the oppressive past of the *Ancien Régime*, but which, instead, summoned back a ballet kind of American fairy tale. *O beata natio!* he said to himself. Great western star, so fortunate in thine origins, so blessed lucky in thy course!

Jefferson, lonely and austere under his Rotunda, was cast appropriately in bronze and — again appropriately — was standing as if, the plans for his University still in his left hand, once more contemplating his fair manor of reason, Monticello. Here was the man whose pen, in deference to "a decent respect to the opinions of mankind," had forever traced the lines that were now enscribed in bronze for all to see:

We hold these truths to be self-evident: that all men are created equal. That they are endowed by their Creator with certain inalienable rights. Among these are Life, Liberty, and the pursuit of Happiness. That to secure these rights Governments are instituted among Men . . .

Documents were dead, but words lived. That night Professor Desmond, sipping a nightcap of gin and tonic, said over to himself once more Jefferson's plangent sentences on liberty and tyranny. He also said aloud two other sentences. The great Biblical: *Watchman, what of the night?* And another watchman's cry when he drops his metal-shod staff on the ringing floor of the Mother of Parliaments: *Who goes home?*

John Desmond was to meet his old friend, Gottfried Krehan, for dinner next evening. Toby, who plumed herself on knowing old Washington quite well, set Professor Desmond down at the *Auberge Chatrian* five minutes ahead of the appointed time, which meant that he was a good quarter of an hour in advance of the so very punctual Dr. Krehan who had, however, to rely on the vagaries of the taxi service of a large American city at the dinner rush hour. Professor Desmond did not mind the delay. It gave him a chance to resume an old acquaintance with Jean Chatrian, proprietor of the *Auberge Chatrian*, whom he had known quite well in the old days twenty years before. It also gave him an opportunity to oversee the preparation of the martinis.

Gottfried Krehan came in, laughing, on the stroke of seven thirty. He gave his hat and cane to a waiter and subsided, still laughing, into a chair.

"You, John," he said, chuckling to himself, "would not care so much. But I wish my old friend, Konrad Adenauer, could have been along."

"Along where, Gottfried?" asked Professor Desmond, handing him a thin-stemmed glass cold-rimed and green-gold translucent in color.

"On my taxi ride," said Dr. Krehan. "Adenauer is a motor *aficionado*, you know. He would rather be Tazio Nuvolari, the driver, or Ettore Bugatti, the designer, than Chancellor of West Germany. Since fate, however, has decreed that he be Chancellor and not winner of the *Prix de France*, by way of compensation he collects taxi drivers."

Dr. Krehan took a deep drink and smacked his lips.

"I, too, collect taxi drivers," he said.

"You do?" said Professor Desmond, amused.

"*Natürlich*," said Gottfried Krehan. "As a student of political ecology, I find it a very valuable pursuit. Taxi drivers are their respective nations in vivid miniature. In Teheran I have ridden with a driver who was straight out of Hafiz. He had roses in silver vases attached to his windshield by suction cups. All Persians are poets at heart. In Mysore I rode with a Hindu driver who sprayed scent on his windscreen every three miles. All Indians, who can achieve that earthly Nirvana, consider themselves great lovers."

"Just where do you place an American taxi driver?" said Professor Desmond, grinning. "Among the aesthetes or the great lovers?"

"Among the great political philosophers," said Dr. Krehan, munching a canapé. "Before I ventured a bet on an American election, I should always consult a taxi driver."

"That's very acute, Gottfried," said Professor Desmond. "What did your taxi oracle say about Americans and Communism?"

"I didn't ask him," said Dr. Krehan. "I answered questions instead. . . . But I can tell you this much, John, on my own. America will never be Communist. Unlike that old Europe of mine."

Dr. Krehan gestured to the murals on the walls of the *Auberge Chatrian.* Jean Chatrian had painted them himself from memories of his native Alsace. He had pictured, affectionately and not at all unskillfully, the spires of Mulhouse. The cathedral of Strasbourg. Obernal. Colmar. The Lion of Belfort. St. Odile's book of prophecy with blue eyes surrealistically superimposed on its open pages.

"But tonight," said Dr. Krehan beginning on a celery stalk, "politics can wait. We talk too much of politics in Europe. I begin to think you talk too much about them even here. Politics can be a disease, my friend. They are the new morphine of the intellectual. They have supplanted art. Art can be a bore, too. Let us make sure neither of those inferior considerations take precedence over the more important pleasures of the table."

Gottfried Krehan ate his dinner down to the very last rich crumb of dessert pastry before sitting back, demitasse in hand.

"Now, John," he said. "Fire away!"

"First," said Professor Desmond, "an indiscreet question. What are you doing in this country, Gottfried? Electronics?"

"The question is not indiscreet," said Dr. Krehan. "No, it is not electronics. I am long since out of that game, John. I am a political, not a physical scientist now. If it were electronics, you may be sure I should not now be living unattended in the *Club Cosmos,* free to come and go as I chose. Above all, I should not at present be sitting here, talking to you. If you really want to know what I am doing here, look at the shoulder insigne of that officer two tables from us. Oh, and John, I am the charge of Chancellor Adenauer's West German Government, not of yours which has so graciously offered me hospitality."

Professor Desmond looked. The insigne was new to him. It was a shield with a torch on it, a stylized horse's head above, below a Latin motto reading: *Veritas et Libertas. Truth and Freedom.*

"You do not know it, eh?" said Dr. Krehan. "It is the insigne of the psychological warfare people. The torch stands for light. You can translate the Latin motto yourself. The horse is the chess knight which, you will remember, can move anywhere and in any direction on the board, and which can, consequently, strike from within enemy territory. The Russians, who play a good deal of chess, will recognize the symbolism. Well, I am in psychological warfare, too. Or so one might say, at least."

Dr. Krehan picked up a brandy bell, sniffed it, then let the amber liquid purl lovingly around his palate.

"If you wish to labor an analogy," he said after a few moments, "psychological warfare might be called a species of electronics of the brain. Your scientists are working now to perfect an electronic brain to power a guided missile. If a companion brain were planted — say, somewhere in the subcellars of the Kremlin — the first brain, launched, say, from Alaska, would try to seek out and find its fellow brain. If and when it did so, there would be an atomic explosion. I am a nonelectronic brain seeking to make contact with other nonelectronic brains — the brains of free minds, that is — in my homeland. The brains, too, of people who are not yet all slave. When we meet, there is quite another kind of explosion, and the Soviet colossus begins to die a little at the top. After the September elections — the end of October, probably — I go to meet again my old friends, Ernst Reuter and Konrad Adenauer. But first, John, I pay a visit to you in Buffalo."

"And Canada," said Professor Desmond.

"Ach, yes! Always I forget Canada. I have never been in Canada."

"You will like it. It is a little like Sweden and Finland. Tell me, Gottfried. Are we facing this Communist thing in the right way here in this country?"

Dr. Krehan's fingers began to drum a tattoo on the table.

"You will please forgive me," he said, "if I speak bluntly. In the main, you do magnificently. But I think you make three basic mistakes. Possibly they are unavoidable mistakes — one of them particularly. Athens made the same mistake when she faced Carthage. I hope that analogy is not too ominous. Let me enumerate them — *so!*"

He placed three bread sticks on the table cloth.

"First," he said, "I am afraid you are too nervous about the middle ground between your own special brand of conservatism and real Communism. I admit the difficulty. It is not always easy to tell. The old Briton, Churchill, puts it admirably: 'It is always a difficult question,' he says, 'to decide at what point Communist intrigues menace the normal freedom of a community, but it is better to be in good time than too late.' It is true one cannot afford to be too late. One cannot afford to trespass too far on 'normal freedom,' either. Second, I do not think you appreciate the real differences which separate the Communist ideologues from the Fascist whom you did understand so well. You think all totalitarians are alike. They are alike in that they are totalitarian and fanatic. But there is a real distinction between the Nazi and Communist demonisms. The one is a perversion of the instincts and the blood stream. The other is a perversion of the mind. . . . But I speak too much. Do I tire you, John?"

For answer Professor Desmond filled the bottoms of the brandy bells once more.

"Go on, Gottfried," he said quietly. "I am intensely interested."

"I do not quite know what to say about this third point," said Dr. Krehan. "It rises out of the degradation of the Soviet thing in practice, and out of the incredible richness of American material life. But, very briefly, let me put it this way. This spring I visited what is called the Lobund Laboratory in one of your great Midwestern Universities. Germ-free guinea pigs and hamsters were being bred there. They were free from but not immune to — an important distinction, I should say — disease. They were quite safe — for the time being. But what if an earthquake should shatter the glass walls of their hygienic world? Then they would be more vulnerable than if they never had been shielded. You follow me so far?"

"Yes," said Professor Desmond.

"Now then," said Dr. Krehan. "Please to look for a moment at the end product of the Soviet system. Soviet man is the man who has learned how to subsist marginally. He is like the kangaroo rat which lives in your dry Southwestern deserts and which gets along without a water supply because it can oxidate its meager food so efficiently. It never comes out into the sun. All day it stays in its burrow because the air there is a little more humid than outside. At night it hops out into the desert to search for seeds and dry plants. It has an amazingly efficient kidney which permits it to drink sea water at need. Its only sweat glands are in the pads on its toes, and it has fewer of these than other rodents. There, John, is the rat adjustment of the new Soviet man Communism has produced. He eats little, drinks nothing, excretes efficiently, and, though he is in a constant state of abject fear, does not sweat. It is hardly a pretty picture. But his survival value is very high. I do not wish to push the analogy too far, but it seems to me that the good life, despite what the television advertisers say, is out of the reach of both hamster and kangaroo rat. Where there is perfect adjustment to environment, there can be no intensity of living. Granted, of course, that the hamster is both more likable and more comfortable behind his hygienic than the kangaroo rat behind his iron curtain."

If Dr. Krehan had looked over his shoulder, he might have seen, four tables behind him, a little dark man who, at a pinch, could have played the part of kangaroo rat even down to looking a little like one. Mr. Tikjan, of course, had more epicurean tastes than the Southwestern American jerboa, genus *Dipodomys*. Since, at the *Auberge Chatrian*, the *spécialités de la maison* were almost exclusively French, and since Mr. Tikjan did not care for French cuisine, he had compromised by ordering a Viennese *lindenschnitte*, a veal slice imprisoned in *soufflé* egg batter, which had the additional merit of being exceedingly reasonable in price.

But Dr. Krehan did not bother to turn his head. He was too busy explaining Marx's dialectical materialism to his friend.

"You know a great deal in this country," he said, "about the organization of the *Agitprops*, the propaganda units of the Party cells. What you have got to learn is something concrete about the dialectical content of *Diamat* itself. There lies the real ideological strength of Communism. Its dialectical materialism is cogent, convincing, and total. And those who cannot follow its fine-spun argumentation are, paradoxically, the most convinced of all."

"It's all balderdash, of course," said Professor Desmond.

"Balderdash?" asked Dr. Krehan. "I do not know this word, 'balderdash.' "

"Balderdash," said Professor Desmond. "Jiggery pokery. Sleight of mouth. Nonsense. *Bloss Verkehrtheit.*"

Dr. Krehan made an almost Gallic gesture of despair.

"You, too, John, with all the rest of them?" he said. "*Verkehrtheit?* Not at all. It is evil, it is wrong, it defiles human nature. But it is not nonsense. In fact, there is no nonsense whatsoever about it, and this fact, perhaps, is its greatest weakness. It is also its main strength. *Diamat* is utterly logical, utterly convincing, utterly seductive, and utterly false."

Professor Desmond looked impressed.

"Communism is a formidable adversary, then," he said.

"I should say so," said Dr. Krehan. "Very formidable indeed. But not invincible. Communism does not take sufficiently into account either the Eastern passion for God or the stubborn and uniquely European conception of the dignity of the human personality. That, I think, will vanquish this new Eastern tyranny as, in its long day, it has vanquished other tyrannies that came out of the East. Darius. Genghis Khan. The Hitlerian Reich. The only trouble is that you, in America, seem to go too fast. And we, in Europe, too slow. Perhaps our tardiness is more dangerous even than your precipitateness."

Professor Desmond looked at his watch.

"It's getting along, Gottfried," he said. "I promised Toby I'd be in before ten. If I'm doomed to be a hamster, I may as well keep hamster hours."

"I, too," said Dr. Krehan, "am a hamster. So I, too, retire early."

Night had fallen along the neon-cozy wharves when the two friends came out of the *Auberge Chatrian,* a dark little man a set number of discreet paces in their rear. Across the street a King Cole in blue tubing and a lobster in red flashed on and off. Along the waterfront other restaurant signs made crimson and emerald snakes of fire in the water. It was as if living colors had been squeezed out of neon tubes onto a shining, moving black palette. Dr. Krehan gestured to them with his cigar.

"I like this sort of thing in your America," he said to Professor Desmond. "It has the seedy brilliance of Van Gogh's billiard room. It is as vital as Montmartre used to be. You must develop a Lautrec now to do it justice."

"Where do you want to be dropped, Gottfried?" asked Professor Desmond, when they were comfortably ensconced in the taxi. "At the *Cosmos Club?*"

"Set me down at the Anacostia Bridge," said Dr. Krehan.

"Oh, come now," said Professor Desmond. "That's too far for a walk to the *Cosmos.*"

"Not at all," said Dr. Krehan. "You forget I used to be an Alpinist. Tonight I wish a long walk. It is early, and the weather is exquisite."

A minute after Professor Desmond's taxi pulled away from the Anacostia Bridge, another pulled up and hastily decanted from its interior a somewhat distrait dark little man. Unlike Dr. Krehan, Mr. Tikjan had never been an Alpinist. Nor did he fancy long walks for sport. But, as a faithful kangaroo rat, he was ready to fulfill his night-time destiny. The information he had so far gleaned this evening was no more than the usual desert quota of a few seeds and some dried leaves. But Mr. Tikjan was a very patient person with a very, very high survival quotient.

On Sunday, with Dr. Krehan in tow, the Desmonds drove to Annapolis for Sunday church. Bells were just ringing down Duke of Gloucester Street for 12 o'clock Mass, when the Desmonds' green Chevrolet ground to a sudden stop in front of the ivy-mantled, sun-flushed red brick of St. Anne's Church at Church Circle. Abandoning his place at the wheel, Professor Desmond leaped out.

"John, dear," said Mrs. Desmond whose knowledge of Annapolis was more intimate than his. "This is the Episcopal church. St. Mary's is down the street a little way."

"That may be," said her husband over his shoulder. "Call it the wrong church, if you want. But it's the right man."

The "right man" was a rosy-gilled, portly rector standing in his church door and conversing with a few last departing parishioners.

Professor Desmond made straight for him and clapped him on the back. Two old Harvardians meeting after two whole decades seem, to the uninitiate, to be speaking pure Wodehouse. Mrs. Desmond managed to catch only the opening salutations. They were enough.

"Tubby!" her husband hailed the rector quite uncanonically.

The clergyman wheeled round. His expression became positively seraphic.

"Hellfire Jack!" he said.

At that catalytic salutation, Toby caught on. This must be the Reverend Dr. Griffith who had shared a study with Professor Desmond at Harvard and who had later gone to the Episcopal Theological Seminary on Brattle Street. They used to exchange Christmas cards once a year but, since the war, Professor Desmond seemed to have lost track of his old roommate. Mrs. Desmond looked with a coolly condescending feminine eye on the tribal caperings. Not so Dr. Krehan. He was, after all, a male, and he, too, in his day, had known ritual attachments to Heidelberg *Mütze* and duelling sabers.

When the ecstasy wore off a little, introductions were made and acknowledged. Then Rector Griffith looked at his watch.

"I take it, Jack," he said, "that you are still a professing member of the Mother Church. My own services are just now over. If you want me to conduct a special one, of course — but no proselyting between friends. It's not sporting, eh? Still. You've only a hundred yards downhill to St. Mary's, but the bells have now stopped ringing and that means Mass is starting. As an interfaith gesture, I make you free of my parking place. That will save a few minutes."

"As another interfaith gesture, Tubby," said Professor Desmond, "how about dinner with us at one-thirty?"

"Excellent," said Rector Griffith, "if, first, you promise to look at a few of the granite coffins here in the churchyard. I want you to see *Margaret, Relict of Charles Carroll,* most especially."

"I'll even take a rubbing, Tubby," said Professor Desmond.

"Also," said Rector Griffith, "I should like to show the children our stained glass windows here. They're the Virgin's Life. We had them cleaned for St. Joachim's Feast last Sunday."

"St. Joachim?" said Professor Desmond blankly.

"The Virgin's father, you know," said Rector Griffith.

"Oh," said Professor Desmond.

"Come along, dear," said Mrs. Desmond. "We'll never get a seat."

They didn't get a seat. But the fan system was efficient, so the church was cool enough. A handsome young midshipman, his crisp blonde hair curled like the head of a Greek statue, got up at once and offered his place to Mrs. Desmond, when he noticed her condition. Professor Desmond watched his wife sitting in the back pew. It was wrong, he thought, to assume men found their wives less lovable when pregnant. Toby looked more lovable than ever now, like a bulky little honey bear, in her present adorable clumsiness.

The organist, who was excellent, played music which Professor Desmond had never heard before. It sounded like *Men of Harlech* to him, but he didn't suppose it could be. During Mass, Dr. Krehan strolled about outside, admiring the fine eighteenth century brick and ironwork of old Annapolis. Just before the Last Gospel, he slipped into the back of the crowded church. Professor Desmond saw him pick up a paper Missal from a pew.

Coming out again into the white light of early noon, Professor Desmond asked his wife what tune it was the organist kept playing throughout the Mass.

"Which one?" asked Mrs. Desmond.

He whistled a few bars.

"That sounds like *Men of Harlech*," she said.

"I thought so, too," he said.

"Except," she said, "that that isn't the tune the organist was playing."

"Oh," said Professor Desmond. "In that case my hypothesis is shattered."

Rector Griffith's stained-glass Life of the Virgin was well worth seeing. The dinner was capital. After cokes all round at Read's, the six of them adjourned to the Naval Academy's Severn front where Professor Desmond got some good color shots, on Grandfather Hansen's movie camera, of the midshipmen sailing out in their small sailboats, another one of the tennis courts in action for Jack's benefit, and still another of the *Reina Mercedes*. Then it was time for some family pictures. Professor Desmond grouped them in various positions until everyone had been shot except himself.

"Here, Sheila," he said, handing her the camera. "Shoot Mother and myself. No more than four feet, though. I want to make sure we get Perry's Lake Erie battle flag in Memorial Hall."

Sheila duly complied with the first part of his instructions. Then, before Professor Desmond could wrest the camera from her, she had trained it on a dark little man who had been lounging against the railing, looking out to sea. The little man was obviously embarrassed. As soon as he noticed the camera pointed toward him, he turned his back and scuttled away.

"Sheila!" shouted Professor Desmond. "Now we won't have any footage for the Perry battle flag!"

"I'm sorry, Dad," said Sheila, surrendering the camera. "I wanted a picture of that jerk. He looks like a chocolate turtle. I saw him before in front of the *Cosmos Club*."

Sheila, not otherwise a notably logical child, was very fond of what the logicians called complete disjunction.

"Either that," she amended thoughtfully, "or it was his twin."

As so often happened in Desmond family situations, Professor Desmond appeared to have forgotten the point originally at issue for another one. In so shifting ground, he glared at Mother. Whenever things went wrong with the children, Professor Desmond had a habit of glaring at Mother.

"Did you hear her, Toby?" he asked. "She used that word again. Jerk! I won't have her using that word. Where in thunder does she pick up expressions like that anyway? On the television cowboy movies? I'll have the set taken out the day we get back."

"I don't think so, John," said Mother pacifically. "It isn't really a cowboy word."

"No," said Moira. "Cowboys use buckaroo talk."

Professor Desmond turned on Moira.

"I won't have buckaroo talk, either," he warned her. "Remember that."

Then he turned back to Mother.

"I suppose she picks it up at school," he said.

"I suppose she does," said Mother.

Mother sounded almost hopeless. It had occurred to her more than once that her husband seemed more interested in the children's grammar than in their fundamental morality.

"You can't very well take her out of school, Jack," said Rector Griffith slily.

"Hmm," said Professor Desmond, ruminating.

"This word — 'jerk,'" put in Dr. Krehan. "I do not know this word. Just what does it mean?"

Professor Desmond thought for a moment.

"*Schelm*," he said. "Only worse."

"They don't use words like that in my grade," said Moira with self-conscious rectitude.

That was the shot that fired Sheila. Dad was one thing. She wanted no sniping from a *franc tireur* only one year her senior.

"They don't in mine, either," she said. "Except the jerks."

"Good God!" said Professor Desmond.

At this point Rector Griffith began to laugh. He laughed till the tears ran down his cheeks and he became utterly helpless.

"I suggest, Jack," he said, between more spasms of laughter, "that we repair to Read's for another round of cokes. This time on me. I thought the chap looked rather like a jerk myself."

Driving back to Silver Springs that evening, Dr. Krehan sat in the front seat with Professor Desmond. He took a silver clipper from his pocket, nipped off the end of a cigar, lit it from the lighter on the dash board, and drew voluptuously on the thin brown cylinder.

"I liked your friend Griffith," he said after a little. "He is a good man, I think. You and he have something, John. Something I have not. Something that beats Communism in the end. An absolute that is nonpolitical, that is outside oneself, and that is above man."

Professor Desmond felt embarrassed.

"You do all right, Gottfried," he said.

"No, John," said Dr. Krehan very seriously. "I mean it. I am like the leper in this morning's Gospel. And unlike him, too. I am a foreigner, I am made clean after the Hitler filth, I am grateful, yet I cannot believe."

Professor Desmond felt more embarrassed than ever.

"It is enough if you are grateful," he said awkwardly. "Never mind about the rest of it."

"No, John," said Dr. Krehan. "To be grateful is something, I admit. It is even much. But it is not enough."

He fished the paper Missal from his pocket.

"I took this from your church this morning," he said. "In exchange for a small bill, of course. It was more than a sentimental gesture. There is something I want to read again from the Last Gospel of John. I like John best of all the Evangelists. Like myself he was a Platonist. You read your great namesake of Patmos, John?"

"Can't say I do," said Professor Desmond stiffly, honking the horn at a passing car.

"No matter," said Dr. Krehan. "You do not need to. You have the habit of belief. Here is what I want to read again. About the Word that dwelt amongst us — men like me worship the word when we worship nothing else. And we saw His glory. And it was *plenum gratiae et veritatis*. Full of grace and truth. Grace, first, you notice, truth after."

"Look, Gottfried," said Professor Desmond, taking one hand from the wheel and patting his knee. "I'd skip this if I were you. Worrying about it won't do any good. You search for truth, don't you?"

Dr. Krehan laughed.

"I think you give me very bad advice," he said. "I do not really worry. I yearn. Yes, I follow *veritas*. I would follow *gratia* also, if I could. Both are necessary, but *gratia* is better. But I cannot, John. I cannot. *Gott hilfe mir, ich kann nicht anders.*"

There was a laconic note from Karen waiting at Silver Springs. It spoke volumes.

Dear Mother, Dad, Moira and Sheila:

How are you and all that stuff? Everything here is O.K. Washed yesterday, and the clothes are even the same color.

Grandmother says Ranee is a nuisance, and Rajah even a bigger one. She doesn't even mention Sillerton Jackson. She almost passed out yesterday when she realized that Moira's shrunken head has been swinging over her bed for two weeks.

Margaret and I beat Bob and Skipper in Badminton double yesterday for the first time, 21–19. Sunday I went to the ball game with Grandfather.

Ellen is fine. There's a letter from Jack saying he'll be home Thanksgiving sure.

It's lonesome pouring milk for only four.

                                        Love,
                                        Karen.

P.S. Please don't mind my e's looking like l's. Or my unsentence-like sentences.

Professor Desmond read the letter aloud.

"Well, half-family," he said, after he had finished. "What's the vote? Had enough of the Southland?"

One could never really get enough of the Southland, but home was best. The vote was unanimous.

Grandmother Hansen did not care for roughing it even in a modified way, so Karen and Kristin were holding the fort on Hurst Monceux instead of at Crescent Beach. As the green Chevrolet hove into sight at eight o'clock in the evening on the twenty-fifth of August, children scattered from the driveway. Rajah and Ranee, purring and inquisitive, sprang on the hood. Kristin came running. Grandfather Hansen waved. Grandmother Hansen kissed Toby when she stepped from the car. Karen kissed her father. Only old Sillerton Jackson, lolling blackly on the back terrace, and red-shocked Bozo did not move. Professor Desmond waved to them anyway.

"O.K., kids," he said. "Shake a leg now, so we can get off to the beach again early in the morning."

CHAPTER EIGHT

The Coming of the Viking

THERE had been portents enough, had anyone chosen to think on them: the Viking masquer on Halloween; what happened in the Bourdon cabin; Karen's dream of the men in armor; the fortune-teller in the amusement park. But no one so chose. The sands ran out of Summer's glass, and the wall separating the two worlds grew thinner. The plane of being tilted for the Desmonds — away from politics, which was one kind of reality, to that of myth, which was another and much realer kind. Myth was simpler and rarer and more courteous. It was archaic, but only as the remembered past was archaic. In love, men and women lived a myth. Children never moved out of myth. That was why, for a few short weeks, Karen had to return to childhood. Though she did not know fully why. . . .

The world of childhood was on another plane than other worlds. Like Alice's universe, it alternately expanded and contracted. It was also a secret world, and, above all, a miniature one. A world like Thumbelina's, still able to envision a walnut shell as cradle, a violet leaf as mattress, a rose petal as coverlet, a tulip leaf as boat. The ivory gates had not yet clashed shut. If it were true that children saw through a glass darkly, it was still a magic glass through which they saw, one through which adults could not see at all. Like the fabled Chinese artist, children were capable of crayoning a cave, then walking into it and being lost to sight for an hour, an afternoon, or a century.

Adolescence was the no-man's, no woman's land, the desolate, terrifying, often piercingly beautiful march that separated the two far countries of childhood and maturity. Across it, roving liaison officers in contact with either camp, rode the children who were no longer children only. Like Karen, sitting now, in blouse, wrist watch, and slacks, portable radio at her feet, an Agatha Christie Pocket Book on her lap, against the great trunk of the huge poplar which had been felled last fall. With her red hair and her blue eyes set wide apart, she might have been a naiad or a dryad, there on the edge of blue water and white sand. She might have been an Undine even, or the tutelary spirit of the vanished tree. The felled poplar was not at all a bad symbol of the great divide the child-woman had now reached. Her childhood had been spent in its shade, in the cool of that murmurous, silver-leaved oasis blooming in the midst of a miniature universe of sand. The leaves were gone now, and the branches. But the tap roots lay deep as ever. Already the stump was putting forth new green shoots.

It may have been Kristin's sandtoys that served as catalyst in the complex reaction that, for a time, brought Karen back to childhood. They lay on the sand at her feet: star of tin, and fish of tin, and tin starfish, too. First she stirred them with a sandaled foot — toenails painted blood-red, to Moira's disgust and Sheila's envy — for just-nine and going-on-eleven are both intolerant and jealous of still-fourteen. Then Karen scooped up the tin fish in one swift surreptitious motion and, languid once again, meditatively bit into it. The remembered metallic taste made childhood surge back with a rush.

It was very strange, when one came to think of it, that, although Sheila and Moira saw the Indians all right, only Karen should have seen the Viking. Because, in spite of her Norwegian name, Karen was the Irish one of the family. Red hair, blue eyes, freckles — a delicate powdering of them across the clear skin — quick temper and all.

But the Viking and the Indians came later. The sword, which was the Viking's, came first, and this is how it came on the August evening of the day Karen condescended to revisit childhood. A sudden summer storm, black with thunderheads, had blown up just after twelve o'clock. It had rained all afternoon, and, during corn-popping, the three older girls had discussed marriage. To keep herself in countenance, Kristin married off two of her paper dolls. Then a

teddy bear and an Easter rabbit. Then Raggedy Ann and Raggedy
Andy. It occurred to Professor Desmond, lounging in a wicker chair,
that Bozo, the eternal bachelor, never seemed to figure in these
nursery epithalamia of Kristin's. Yet Bozo did not exactly have what
one would describe as a celibate's face. Perhaps, thought Professor
Desmond ribaldly to himself, here was another case like the case of
the Phoenix, the Arabian bird, which was chaste perforce because
it was the only one of its kind. At least, he had never heard of a
Mrs. Bozo.

It was inevitable that the discussion should turn to honeymoons.
Karen, some years nearer to the mysterious possibility than Moira or
Sheila, offered it as her opinion that Norway first, then Ireland,
would be the perfect honeymoon tour.

"I," said Moira, "am going to India to see Mr. Yeddanapalli."

As she poured more melted butter on the tiny cotton bolls of
popcorn, Moira looked more like a little blonde Indian than ever
with her flaxen pigtails and strangely slanting blue eyes so like
Mother's, except that Mother's were brown. Mr. Yeddanapalli, a
Hindu gentleman from Madras, had taught chemistry two years
before at their father's college. All three older girls had loved his
Rajah's profile and his bronze skin, and Kristin had highly esteemed
his silver flute. But Mr. Yeddanapalli had been the very apple of
Moira's eye.

"I," said Sheila more practically, "will go first to New York, and
then to Boston."

On the marriage *Bourse* Sheila could have been described as all
American in looks and all American in ambition. The only old-
world magical thing about her heart-shaped face was that it had one
brown and one green eye. Karen had read somewhere in a book that
the French, who had a reputation for being knowing in these matters,
called this *le regard de Vénus*. The Venus look.

"How does one get to go on a honeymoon?" asked Kristin, looking
up from her paper doll nuptials.

From the height of her superior awareness Karen grinned. It was
really great fun, this looking again through the uncomplicated, yet
keen eyes of childhood.

"Babar and Celeste took a balloon," she said.

It was the family weakness again for literary allusion. Sometimes, for three nights running, Moira and Sheila did a new play for which Karen used to supply the lines. The plays were always different, but there were two stock parts which, as in the case of the Italian pantomime, never varied. Sheila, who could pirouette, was a Dancing Doll or a Sugar Plum Fairy. Moira, who couldn't, a Wooden Soldier or a Jumping Jack. But plays were evening games, except for days dark with driving winter blizzards which closed all the Buffalo schools and turned afternoon into evening. Having a play at the beach on an end of August afternoon, even during a shower, seemed a bit too much like cheating. So the dismal cry of childhood growing older began for the first time that summer.

"What shall we do?"

"We can play school," said Moira doubtfully.

There was no doubt whatsoever in Sheila's answer.

"No," she said flatly. "I think playing school is horrid."

And then, as a sort of afterthought, a mental exercise in which Sheila was a specialist:

"I think school is horrid, too."

"We can do eurythmics," said Karen, poising her arms theatrically for the upbeat and the downbeat.

"Ar-sis," she chanted. "And the-sis. The-sis and ar-sis."

Sheila wrinkled her little nose.

"That's goony," she said.

Then Moira had an inspiration.

"Let's play Uncle Charlie's game," she said.

Uncle Charlie's game was digging for buried treasure. They hadn't played it for some time because, when one turned up nothing but shells and an occasional old bottle top, digging even for buried treasure could become very boring. Somehow, when Uncle Charlie wasn't around, sea shells and old bottle tops were all one did manage to turn up. Only Uncle Charlie seemed to know where the pennies and nickels and, once in a blue moon, the quarters were likely to have been left — in Uncle Charlie's version, at least — by the wicked pirates who had formerly infested the white curving sands of Crescent Beach.

It was Karen, years beyond the age of make-believe, who found the sword in Gorham's field. Tolerantly she had fallen in with Moira's sudden whim. It was even at her suggestion that the three of them

had tried a new digging place. Whether it was that the rain had
left the beach too chilly and too unpleasantly damp; or that she
had once found two arrowheads in the field behind the tracks; or
whether, practical miss that she was underneath, she remembered
how one might come across wild strawberries there even if one didn't
come upon treasure; or whether, finally, as she herself afterward
thought, something told her to search at the base of the oak — at
any rate, whatever the explanation, it was right there under the
Gorham oak that they turned up the sword.

It was a piece of good luck in itself to find even a few strawberries
this late in the season. They tasted especially delicious after the
rain: tiny red arrowheads of sharp sweetness with drops of water
still cool on the notched green-shafted tips of strawberry leaves.
Moira and Sheila ate ten apiece. Then, under Karen's direction, the
three of them set to work with their sand shovels, which had been
borrowed from Kristin's considerable arsenal of such implements,
just to the right of the great oak tree. There was a sizable excavation
there already where Dr. Thibault, whose rock garden blazed in
glorious bloom all spring, all summer, and well into the fall, had
taken his last load of topsoil. Without speaking, they dug doggedly
for a time in the dark, rich loam.

A train shrilled past on the Grand Trunk track. Auto horns
sounded, far off and muted, from the Dominion Highway running
inland from the lake. The western sky passed from crimson to mauve
behind them. Mist began to gather in the hollows of the field, and
the first evening mosquitoes struck up their humming song. There
was a deep-toned tonk-tonk of cowbells as the Gorham cows headed
for their barn. Then, as if answering the cowbells, Karen's blade
clinked on something metal.

"Girls!" she said excitedly. "I've struck treasure!"

It was the sword. But it took twenty minutes more hard digging
before it was completely uncovered and even then, what with the
rust and mold of ages, it didn't look much like treasure.

"Why," said Sheila, disappointed, "it's just a nasty piece of iron."

Karen's pulses began to pound like little drums. For a minute she
turned almost faint.

"Just wait till we clean it," she said. "Things get dirty when
they've lain in the earth for heavens knows how many centuries."

"But what is it?" asked Moira, eyeing the rusted thing with some distaste.

"I think," said Karen, the roof of her mouth dry with an obscure kind of excitement. "I think it's a sword. Father is sure to know."

Professor Desmond did know. When the girls told him how and where they had found the sword, he grew quite excited and began to jot down things in a little leather notebook. Then he took certain books off the pine wood shelves. Rather dull ones, Moira thought, with their tedious maps and diagrams. No proper pictures at all, and no conversations, either. Books by men with such uninteresting names as Gathorne-Hardy and Hjalmar Holand, and such unpromising titles as *The Norse Discoveries and Explorations in America.*

While Professor Desmond consulted his books, Mrs. Desmond polished vigorously. Soon the sword, now recognizably a sword, lay there on the dining room table under the old-fashioned green lamp. The blade was long, heavy, and double-edged. The hilt was fashioned of bronze. Two crossed battle-axes were carved on one side of the crossbar. On the other side was the head of a bearded man in a helmet. Professor Desmond put down his pipe and hefted the weapon.

"You know, dear," he said to Mother in an abstracted tone almost as if the children were not in the room, "this is very like the sword they dug up in Minnesota — the one the Smithsonian calls the Ulen sword. I should very much like to show this to Krehan. He used to be interested in this sort of thing."

"There should be no difficulty about that, John," said Mrs. Desmond. "We can show it to him when he comes in September. I think he said September."

"Or early October," said Professor Desmond, still thinking hard. Yes, we can show it to him then. It will have to be up here, though. We can't very well take the thing over the Peace Bridge into Buffalo. Not yet, anyway. You see, there is the question of the Canadian Government. Is the sword ours or theirs? Or is it Mr. Gorham's? If it is treasure trove, it's theirs. If it turns out to be what I think it is, it's a national monument, and so again it's theirs. If not, it's nothing, and we don't want it, either. If it's nothing, you can be sure Mr. Gorham won't be much interested."

"Obviously, it's something, John," said Mother mildly.

Professor Desmond thought it was something all right. He walked up and down excitedly.

"By George!" he said, turning again to Mother. "This could be the discovery of the century. I wonder if it ties in with the folk-tale analogue I went to Christian Island about."

"I wouldn't know, John," said Mrs. Desmond. She felt suddenly troubled, almost as if the sword were an evil omen.

Her husband thoughtfully hefted the thing again. "Hm'm," he said, "the oak is Thor's tree."

"I thought it was Mr. Gorham's tree," said Sheila. "It's in his field."

"So it is," said Mother. "What Father means is that Thor was a pagan god of ancient Norway. Your great-great-grandfather, Thor Henrikson, was named after him."

"But what has that got to do with the oak tree in Mr. Gorham's field?" asked Sheila practically.

"It may have a great deal to do with it," said Professor Desmond slowly. "There are three ash trees at the field's edge, too."

This was a new twist for her rationalist husband. Mrs. Desmond's sense of uneasiness deepened.

"If you're looking for magic trees, John," she said, "what about the thorn tree by the railway hedge?"

Professor Desmond's mood changed at once.

"So you don't think oak, ash, and thorn are trees of power?" he said. "What is, then, in the name of Rudyard Kipling?"

"For me," said Mrs. Desmond half seriously, "the chestnut. It has tiny silver-white candelabra in the spring, and in the fall they all turn into tiny live red coals — but cool ones — burning brave on their green braziers."

"That," said Professor Desmond, looking at his wife with tender mockery, "is poetic enough to mark the child. We don't need another poet in the house, you know. What we really need is a rich brewer."

Mother laughed.

"Maybe the O'Keefe's will take care of marking him that way," she said. "There's enough of it around."

Before Professor Desmond snapped off the downstairs lights for the night, he set the sword squarely in the middle of the gray stone mantel where, in the late Canadian springs, Mother used to place huge clumps of purple lilac in her favorite bowl of bronze that had frogs worked on it in cunning relief. It was full of little early chrysanthemums now. He pushed it to the left so that the tip of the sword blade just touched the curve of the bronze.

That evening the first chill of fall blew in from the lake. It was only a few days now to Labor Day and school again and the beginnings of those red-coal chestnut windfalls Mrs. Desmond loved so well. Professor Desmond lit the heater in the girls' room where Moira and Sheila slept. Karen's and Kristin's room got some of the warmth that went up the stair well from the downstairs fireplace.

After brushing her teeth, Karen lingered a minute or two in the cozy little upstairs bathroom that looked out over miles of water to the far off American shore. The casement window always made her think of the cabin of the *Hispaniola*. Tonight the lake looked angry and cold. White caps crested as far out as the eye could reach. Seventy-five feet below her great waves began to plunge against the retaining wall. A steady flow of air surged loud through the poplars. Karen shivered a little as she climbed into bed.

That night Karen had another strange dream which somehow seemed connected with the one she had had Christmas week, the one about the dead Sea King and his son. She was standing in the prow of a very odd ship which, because of its resemblance to Mother's bronze dragon-ship model on the mantel at home, she recognized as an old Norse galley. Spray kept dashing in her face, and higher up into the lidless eyes of the dragonish figure that loomed above her, its snaky tongue forked out as if to taste the stinging salt. A strange woman, very tall and very beautiful, stood by Karen, one white hand on her shoulder, steadying her each time the ship plunged heavily into the sickening trough of yet another wave. Somehow she knew that the strange lady's name was Sigrid. If she ever saw her again, and somehow she was sure she would, Karen thought she would be able to recognize her by the bracelet on her rounded arm. It was a spray of silver leaves and berries, each leaf and berry exquisitely clear and shining with the soft sheen of moonlight on a mist-marbled lake.

"Courage, little kinswoman!" said the strange and beautiful Sigrid. "Courage! There are heavy seas ahead!"

In the morning the air was quite chilly. A few first yellowing leaves drifted down from the poplars when the three older girls went to the backyard pump for drinking water. As, carrying back the pail down the board walk, she yawned sleepily, Karen wondered if her dream had anything to do with the sword. As it turned out, it had. A great, great deal.

The adventure of the sword began again, three and a half weeks later, on the evening of the day Moira was so cross about Sheila's glasses. They were motoring along the King's Highway Friday afternoon to spend their last September week end at Crescent Beach, where Dr. Krehan was scheduled to meet them at supper. They had just passed the *Steaks n' Shakes* shack, soon to be shuttered up till spring, when Moira launched her attack.

"Sheila," she announced vehemently out of nowhere, "looks awful in her glasses."

The glasses were new, they were butterfly-harlequin in design, and plaid in color. Sheila thought she looked perfectly ravishing in them. They had been expensive enough.

"I do not look awful!" said Sheila, her voice rising in crescendo wail.

"Shh!" said Mother. "I want Kristin to get a little snooze so she can stay up a bit later tonight for Dr. Krehan's first evening."

It was then and there that Professor Desmond made his tactical error, possibly because he was still hot and flustered from clearing three cats, for the third time that summer, past the Canadian Immigration authorities — two of the cats Siamese and, consequently, incorrigibly intimate with people who peered through car windows. The Immigration inspector, a confirmed ailurophobe, had gotten the scare of his life. So now Professor Desmond, who had come off second best in the recent exchange of personalities, forgot the immutable household law that one did not argue with Moira — that is, one did not argue and win.

"Of course she doesn't!" he snapped. "Sheila looks exceedingly pretty in her glasses. Ingrid Bergman wears glasses, too — horn-rimmed ones."

It would have been a clever thrust against either of the other two older children, since all three of them had seen Miss Bergman in her Technicolor *Joan of Arc,* and admired her greatly. But not against Moira.

"Joan of Arc didn't wear glasses," she stated categorically.

"Of course she didn't," said Professor Desmond patiently. "Glasses hadn't yet been invented."

"That's why I like Joan of Arc then," said Moira. "She didn't wear glasses."

Professor Desmond's patience was wearing thin. He began to drive faster. The car bounced. Old Sillerton Jackson dug his fore claws into the seat upholstery to maintain his balance.

"Didn't I just finish telling you," he said angrily "that, to the best of my knowledge, no one in the later Middle Ages — in Europe, at least, I believe they had got round to them in China — wore glasses for the good and simple reason that medical science had not yet evolved them?"

Moira's jaw was set now just like her father's.

"Yes," she said, "you did. And that's why I like the olden days best. Because then *no one* had to wear those awful glasses."

There was a blank silence. Professor Desmond's left hand began to tap the wheel.

"John, dear," said Mother quietly, "Joan of Arc or not, do you think you ought to hold up Ingrid Bergman as a model any more? After all, there's Rossellini."

"What," said Professor Desmond with ominous precision, "is wrong with Rossellini? Or would you prefer me to invoke Zsa Zsa Gabor instead? Or Marilyn Monroe?"

His hand continued to tap the wheel and his foot to press the accelerator. The car had, by now, turned off the little tarred road running alongside the railroad tracks, and lurched into the cottage back yard. The tires squealed to an abrupt stop. Professor Desmond took both hands off the wheel now and slewed round to glare at Moira in the back seat. Mrs. Desmond tapped him on the arm.

"Look, John," she said diplomatically. "Mr. Szabo's pinned a telegram to the back screen."

Mr. Szabo was the Hungarian gentleman who ran the General Store and Soda Fountain across the tracks. He also had a pay telephone. Out-of-season telegrams were always delivered to him for transshipment to their lawful recipients.

Professor Desmond tore open the telegram.

"Oh damn!" he said, after reading it.

Mrs. Desmond was too interested in finding out what the telegram contained to say anything at all about her husband's using his forbidden word.

"What's the matter, John?" she asked anxiously. "Isn't Dr. Krehan coming?"

"He's coming all right," said Professor Desmond. "Only he can't stay longer than the week end. His plane leaves New York for Berlin the middle of next week."

"Then," she said, "we'll just have to pack as much as we can into the week end. At least, we've plenty of provisions."

"I'm very disappointed," said Professor Desmond. "I wanted plenty of time to talk about the sword."

"You'll have enough time for that at any rate," said Mrs. Desmond. "Tell me, John. What does Dr. Krehan like especially? I know so little about him in spite of our day together at Annapolis. Did he stay in Germany all through the war?"

"Oh, no," said Professor Desmond. "Didn't I ever tell you? He left Germany originally during the Hitler terror. Stayed with the Russians for a time before moving on to England and then the States. Something went wrong in Russia — nothing that bothers our Security people, though. Krehan was never a Red. He never talks of those days. Got the Nobel for Physics sometime in the thirties. Out of science now and in politics, instead. A thoroughly admirable fellow. Salt of the earth."

Again, as in the case of the sword, a chill premonition went through Mrs. Desmond.

"John," she said, "in view of Dr. Krehan's past, do you think it's dangerous for him to go about as he does?"

Professor Desmond looked quizzically at his wife.

"Unattended, you mean, Toby?" he asked. "That's very acute of you. Maybe you do have something at that. I hinted the same thing to Krehan the night we were at Chatrian's place. He told me he was the responsibility of his government, not of mine. So I had to let it go at that."

"I suppose it's all right," said Mother hesitantly. "I shouldn't want anything to go wrong while he's with us. There are the children, too, to consider."

Aha! he said to himself, a little amused now. The wind lay in that quarter all the time. The mother chicken and her chicks.

"It's O.K., Toby," he said. "I don't think there's really anything to worry about."

"I suppose not," she said more cheerfully. "Have we everything he needs?"

Professor Desmond thought again.

"At Bonn," he said, "Gottfried liked beer. Probably still does. Guess I'd better drive back to the Brewery before it closes."

He turned to the three older girls.

"Who wants to come?"

Sheila and Moira did. Kristin went along as a matter of course, without even being asked. Karen preferred to go down to the beach. It was one of the few chances she got nowadays to be alone, and she had reached the reflective age when, once in a while, she liked being alone. Besides, September and October were her favorite months for walking along the water's edge.

Crescent Beach had its points of beauty in any season, even in midwinter when the northern ice-pack strode straight up to the wall. In early spring, after the ice was gone, but before the first faint cloud of green misted the poplars and the lilac bushes, it seemed to Karen that their lake cottage stood at the end or else at the beginning of the world. The air was so still, not even a gull calling; the water so sweet and pure and cold where it lapped over the rippled corduroy of the sand. Later on in spring the far right horn of the crescent ran wild with reeds and marsh grass. The poplars grew so lush and thick there that at a distance one could almost believe oneself in the tropical jungle world of the giant lizards. When Karen told this fancy of hers to her father, he didn't laugh at all. He said Lake Erie looked much the same now as in the time of the great saurians which, when you came to think of it, were only unbelievably large toads. Then Professor Desmond had had his first-born red-headed daughter get down on her knees close to a toad's golden eyes. It had given her a funny turn at the time. But ever since then she had had a very vivid idea of how a tyrannosaurus rex must have looked to a diplodocus, she having played the part of a diplodocus to a toad's tyrannosaurus. Sometimes, too, when the gray lake fogs rolled in over the beach and the fog horns began their hoarse yearning, it was almost as if great saurians sobbed and lamented in the mist. *Mmmm-*UH, they grieved. *Mmmm-*UH.

But September and October were far and away the best. It wasn't only that the glorious week ends stolen from the weekday rhythm of school were sweeter far than the slow wheeling summer weeks which, in June, seemed to stretch ahead forever and then were so suddenly over. Nor was it alone the great yellow watch-face of the hunter's moon. September and October were the Indian months when the bronze poplars marched, single file, down to the shore. When all the oaks had their war paint on. When the smoke of autumn's campfires went up and up and up forever into the motionless heavens.

Today was especially beautiful; bright and still and clear. There would be mist over the waters later, as evening drew on. But that would do no more than make the bell buoy out in the steamer channel sound the farther off and so, to Karen's ear, more fairy like than by day. She skipped a stone or two in the cool stillness, and then went back to the house to help Mother with the dinner.

Their guest arrived by taxi from Fort Erie just as Professor Desmond came back from the Brewery with a case of O'Keefe's. Dr. Krehan brought Scandinavian dolls for the three older girls. A Norwegian maiden for Sheila. A Danish girl for Moira. And for Karen, so far past the age of dolls that it was beginning over again with whatnot puppets, a little Lapp girl dressed, like the Robber Girl in *The Snow Queen*, in soft leather boots and with a tiny knife at her belt. Kristin got a rubber frog for her bath. It whistled when one squeezed it hard. A gentle pressure on the waistcoat button made the frog's red tongue pop out quite impolitely but most amusingly.

Dr. Krehan seemed a very quiet man to Karen. Although he must know Mother quite well by now, he bowed from the waist when Mrs. Desmond put out her hand. He also bowed — not quite so low, however — to the girls. For the two he knew already there was an additional twinkle of the eye and a merry wink. At supper the grownups talked of politics which, as usual, Karen found uninteresting; and of war, but after a fashion which she did not understand any too well. Once Mother said something in reference to Dr. Krehan's work on the German election laws. Professor Desmond looked hard at her in the meaning sort of way he had whenever he wanted a subject dropped. So Mrs. Desmond said nothing further about that especial topic.

After coffee, Kristin took the center of the stage for a little while. She was wearing her blue sweater suit with all the buttons on it. Karen noticed that Dr. Krehan appeared to like children. What was more, they liked him. He danced Kristin on his knee; then counted her buttons aloud.

"Kristin," said Sheila, "is going to be a Beggarman."

"So?" said Dr. Krehan in his faintly foreign accent. "How do you make that out?"

"Count them again," said Sheila. "I'm a lawyer."

"Of the Philadelphia variety," interjected Professor Desmond. "Ask Moira what she is."

"I," said Moira, "am a Chief."

"Fire Chief or Indian?" asked Dr. Krehan.

"Indian, of course," said Moira a little disdainfully.

"Ja," said Dr. Krehan, smiling. "It would for you be Indian. Do you know, Moira, in the country where I was born we used to have a wider choice than you? On baby buttons anyway."

He counted out a little folk rhyme in German on Kristin's blue sweater.

"*Kaiser, König, Edelmann, Bürger, Bauer, Bettelmann, Schuster, Schneider, Leineweber, Doktor, Kaufmann, Totengräber.* That means, little Moira, though it does not go so nicely in English: *Emperor, King, Nobleman, Townsman, Farmer, Beggarman, Shoemaker, Tailor, Linen Weaver, Doctor, Merchant, Undertaker.*"

Dr. Krehan was silent for a moment. Then he looked across at Mother. When he spoke again, his voice sounded strange.

"You know, Mrs. Desmond," he said, "I have not said that since my childhood which, perhaps, is not so very odd. But it will be strange, I think, returning to my Fatherland next week. My tongue has grown rusty in the years I've been away. But not, I think, my heart."

One of the grown-up silences, which children never understood and which always made them uneasy, settled over the supper table. Sheila fixed her eyes on her plate. Moira looked at Karen. Professor Desmond looked at his wife. No one looked at Dr. Krehan, except Kristin. He went on talking as if to himself, as if no one were there. Very softly.

"It is very odd when one comes to think of it. First went *Kaiser, König, Edelmann,* and never came back. Then, one by one, the others went — all but the *Bettelmann* and the *Totengräber.* Now no one but *Bettelmänner* and *Totengräber* live in the land where once I lived. In the East marches, that is. In the West, it is better. But everywhere the alien rules, East or West."

Dr. Krehan looked up.

"Forgive me, my friends," he said, embarrassed. "You must think me a foolish old sentimentalist. Also, you must not think I do not love this new land of yours which is my host. After all, did I not help America prepare the great bomb that might so easily have been used against people I once knew and who, perhaps, have not entirely forgotten me? But I do no more of that kind of thing. Now I work for peace, not for war. And for the healing of my wounded country."

Professor Desmond, with a little cough, broke a fresh new pack of cigarettes out of its cellophane. He passed them around. Dr. Krehan shook his head. He took a thin cigar out of an old-fashioned case, nipped off its head with a silver cutter, lighted it, and put it in his mouth. Then he picked Kristin up again.

"Now, my little friend," he said briskly. "I will teach you a livelier song."

He danced her on his knee, as if the child were cantering astride a hobby horse.

> "Hop! Hop! Hop!
> Kristin lauft galop!
> Über Stock und über Steine
> Kristin bricht mir keine Beine!
> Hop! Hop! Hop!
> Kristin lauft galop!"

Dr. Krehan blew three smoke rings into the air, one after another, then set Kristin down. She ran over to her mother.

After that the children went upstairs to bed in the little ship's cabin bedroom under the sloping eaves. All but Karen, that is. She stayed a while, listening to the grownups talk. They talked of books, which she liked. And, as at supper, of politics, which she didn't. But one of the many things Dr. Krehan had to say interested her.

"You of the West," he said to Professor and Mrs. Desmond, "even yet do not understand either the North or the East European — for good or for bad. You get some insights, I suppose, into the good side of the Russian in the glorious women of Tolstoi and Turgenev. But how many, after all, read Tolstoi or Turgenev? You know from Grimm the childlike quality of the German. From Grimm and from this Hummel woman whose bric-a-brac is so popular in this country."

"She was a nun," said Professor Desmond, "and she is dead."

"So?" said Dr. Krehan. "I did not know. To resume. The world, to its sorrow — as a German, I freely admit it — has learned that the German can be Hagen as well as Hansel. It is beginning to learn that the new man of the Soviet can be as fanatic as a Moslem warrior on *Jihad*. Do you recall what Colonel Lawrence said of the Arabs? That they were a dogmatic people, seeing the contours of things only in black and white with 'a universal clearness or hardness of belief, almost mathematical in its limitation.' "

"That's very good, Gottfried," said Professor Desmond, nodding his head.

"I do not say this to condemn them, John," said Dr. Krehan. "Lawrence admired this quality in his Arab. As an attitude, it is a neutral thing. It can be channeled for good or for evil. It has great loyalty, great self-sacrifice, great generosity in it. You know the Viking sagas, John, much better than I do. Do you remember the *Lay of Authun?*"

Again Professor Desmond nodded.

"There," said Dr. Krehan enthusiastically, "is the Russian essence for you. And the German, too, in all its feudal naïveté, its unsophistication. In Authun, Viking of the northwest fjords, who gave all his treasure to own a white bear, because he had never

seen anything so wondrous. When Harald of Norway heard of the
bear, he offered the Icelander double what he gave for the animal
in the first place. But Authun answered that the bear was a present
for his own lord, Sveinn of Denmark. And both kings honored
Authun for his great loyalty. After that he was called the luckiest
of men because he had the best liege lords."

"That's the joker, Gottfried," said Professor Desmond. "Neither
Joe nor Adolf were exactly good liege lords."

"I agree," said Dr. Krehan. "But the good potential is still
there. It only needs educing."

Then their discussion turned away from Vikings and became
abstract again. Karen soon tired of it.

It was her after-supper task to gather up the leavings from the
plates and empty them into the metal receptacle near the great
white boulder at the back of the Desmond property only a few
yards or so from the narrow tarred road which ran between the
houses and the railroad tracks.

She came out into a late September night of silver magic. Mist
beaded the dark shingles of the roof. Far out on the lake the bell
buoys swung. Their tune was as silver as the September moon
which paid out its silvern coin everywhere. On the still water and
white sand. On the bronzed poplar leaves and pale birch trunks.
On the shining boulder . . .

Mr. Sillerton Jackson saw him first. Despite his age, the old cat
still liked to mouse a little of an evening near the boulder where,
because of the refuse, the hunting was likely to be good. Now,
very suddenly, he skittered sideways like a kitten chasing a leaf.
Then stood stock still, staring at the rock, his forelegs trembling
a little. Karen followed the gaze of the cat's green eyes to the great
white stone. Then she too, started.

The Viking was sitting cross-legged on the boulder. He was very
tall and very strong, with a golden beard like the beard of Arthur
in Moira's *Boy's Book of King Arthur.* There were silver bands
around his muscled upper arms, and meshed chain mail rose and
fell to the rhythmic breathing of a stalwart chest. His legs were
bare except for moccasins of Indian buckskin. Karen knew his face
at once under the winged helmet. It was the bearded profile on
the cross bar of the mysterious sword. It was also the face of the

extra masquer at Jack's Halloween party. And the face of the Sea King's son in her dream.

The moon shone clear on the pensive warrior. From her post within the velvet blackness of the poplar shadow, Karen stepped forward into the luminous whiteness and waited expectantly. Still he seemed not to see her. Or at least, if he did see her, not to notice or let on. A new thing in her little life, a wave of sheer maleness, of good sex and the power of good sex, shook her for a moment. A sudden instinct to coquet came over her with a rush, to be abandoned at once for an even older primordial impulse, that of the maid's obeisance before the hero. Of Nausicaa before godlike Odysseus. Of Desdemona before Othello. Of Desdemona who loved him for the dangers he had passed, and he loved her that she did pity them. She had no sense of unreality, no impression of dream state. She knew she was awake, and that what she looked on was as real as herself. Only she walked on another plane than the plane of everyday.

Karen thought for a few seconds. Surely one did not offer to shake hands with an ancient Norseman — this time from the very outset Karen knew that the Viking had stepped out of time. Or did one? Instead, she dropped him a little curtsey such as she had seen the maids-in-waiting do to Princess Elizabeth in the Technicolor motion pictures of the royal wedding. It struck her as being most appropriate.

As she dropped him the curtsey, something else came into her mind.

"*God Jul,*" said Karen to the musing Viking.

She had picked it out of her father's phrase book, *Beginning Norwegian*. It did not, of course, suit the occasion perfectly, since it was modern Norse for *Merry Christmas*, and Christmas was still three months off. But, under the circumstances, saying anything at all in Norse to an age-old Viking she had seen before but never met had to be considered in the nature of an accomplishment.

Apparently the Viking thought so, too. In utter astonishment he turned and focused a piercing glance on the young girl.

"By the hammer of Thor my patron!" he said at last. "Nine hundred years waiting on this lonely shore and tonight, for the first time, a little New World maid speaks to me in the ancient tongue!"

Karen, who had once met one of her Norse cousins, a salmon
fisher from the Columbia River who spoke English with a heavy
Norwegian accent, thought that, for a Norseman born and bred, the
Viking spoke pretty good English. Still and all, perhaps it was
not to be much wondered at. Nine hundred years was a long time.
If he hadn't already forgotten them, most likely the Viking spoke
Spanish, Portuguese, French and Dutch equally well, to mention
only the colonizing tongues, to say nothing of several Indian lan-
guages, including a few dead ones.

The Viking got off his boulder and gravely gave her one huge
hand.

"What," he asked, "may your name be, little New World
maiden?"

Not so little and not so young, thought Karen to herself a trifle
resentfully. But she curtsied again, for a sense of awe was still
strong upon her.

"Karen Desmond, sir," she said in a low voice.

"Karen," said the Viking, patting her hand. "It is a good name.
It is a name from my own *vik* where we used to beach the long
ship when the ice pack grew too thick. But Desmond — that is the
sort of outlandish name Duke Rollo's sons brought back from
Frankland which you call France."

"Father says it is an Irish name," said Karen politely.

The Viking laughed aloud.

"Oho!" he said, still laughing. "The Irish! That would explain
the freckled skin, the blue eyes which are not Norse blue, and the
red hair which is not Norse red. You are not entirely a daughter
of my fjords, little maiden. I mind me of the bare-legged, red-haired
Irish moppets who would fling stones at our shield wall on the
gunwales, as we rowed into Dublin Bay to bring spearmen to Duke
Sitric. You look not unlike them, my skinny red-haired friend."

Ordinarily Karen was the politest of young ladies. But she could be
very sensitive about her red hair and slim legs. In a quick flash,
she stooped, picked up a pebble, and flung it against the Viking's
mailed chest off which it bounced with a tiny clang.

"Aha!" said the Viking. "Things do not change much, I see, with
the Irish. I might as well be back in Dublin Bay."

"There is no place for you in Dublin Bay any more," she said.

"For you or any other foreigner. My history book says that King Brian drove out the Norsemen in 1014."

"Aye," said the Viking grimly. "So long ago as that? I had not remembered it was so long ago. It seems but yesterday I saw the carnage. I was there at Clontarf. The Irish Queen of Sitric laughed from the battlements as our men died."

"That was not very polite of her," said Karen, honor satisfied. "I, too, am sorry for being impolite. I should not have thrown the stone."

"No offense taken, little maiden," said the Viking, clapping her on the shoulder. "We are quits. Besides, I like a little spirit in a girl. Nor was I over polite myself, especially in view of the fact that my grandmother was Maeve of Ireland, and Ciartan her father's name before. But there is one thing still puzzles me, Karen Desmond. How is it you can see me? Nine hundred years and more now have I been on this desolate shore. Generations of men and women and children have come and gone, both red and white. But never until this very night has anyone seen me, no, not since the day when — "

The Viking was silent for a space. He shivered a little.

"You *do* see me, little red one?" he asked her.

"Oh, yes," said Karen. "Perfectly. I have seen you before, too. You are the warrior whose face is carved on the sword guard. I saw you at a party in this house last year. Once I saw you in a dream."

"Oh, the sword," said the Viking. "Yes, the sword. It is my sword, you know. Asgrim of Lillehammer smithied it for me — Asgrim the greatest armorer in all the Northland. I saw you dig it up at the foot of the oak — you and your sisters. The little one with the smooth brown face, and the blond one like a little troll. A very little, and sometimes a very angry troll."

He laughed to himself.

"If I only had my drinking horn with me," he said, "I would drink a toast to that one. I would say: *Skål, Skål, lille trold!* Which means taken from the ancient tongue: *Skoal! Skoal! Little troll!* But we shall speak later of my sword, you and I. Just now I want to know how it is you can see me. What do you think the reason may be, little red one?"

Karen thought hard.

"Perhaps," she said courteously, "it is because I was born with a caul."

"I, too," announced the Viking in delight, "was born with a caul."

He stopped, sobered.

"But," he said, after an interval. "That cannot be the cause. The Guardians of the Portals have other and better reasons for their doings. Besides, it was not I who had the second sight in the family. It was Sigrid, my sister, who had gotten that strange gift of the Norns. I mind me now she read the runes for me once, before I sailed on that last voyage from which I never returned. She stared into the coals on Christmas Eve and said, her teeth chattering with fear, that I should see things no man of all our race had ever seen, and that, one day in the far future, at the hither end of time, I should meet, on the shore of an inland ocean, a little kinswoman who should recover for me the sword the savages should steal. Then, at last, I could be at rest."

The Viking stared at Karen.

"By the hammer of Thor my patron!" he burst out. "You must be that little kinswoman of mine!"

He knelt at the girl's feet and kissed her hand.

"Sigrid," said Karen regally to him, like a Queen, no longer just a girl not yet in her middle teens. "Sigrid. I think I saw her in a dream last night. She was tall and beautiful, and she stood in the prow of a dragon ship."

"Many women are tall and beautiful," said the Viking, disappointed. "And all our ships have dragon prows. Can you remember anything she wore or anything she said?"

"She said: 'Courage, little kinswoman! There are heavy seas ahead,'" said Karen, wrinkling her forehead in an effort to remember. "Her arm was round and white, and on it she wore a silver spray of leaves and berries."

"Eirik's morning gift!" shouted the Viking, striking his head with his great gauntleted hand. "He gave it to her the morning of their wedding. I was his groomsman and rode to Laagen with the bridal party. You are the kinswoman of Sigrid of Laagen, and so my cousin, too. I am Thorbjorn of Whale's Ness, Karen Desmond.

Thor the Bear. I salute you across the centuries."

The Viking embraced the girl.

"Goodness me . . ." said Karen, embarrassed, for she was already some years past the age when girls accepted caresses as a matter of course. "Your armor's very prickly. It's true Grandfather Hansen came from Laagen near where they found the Oseberg Ship. Mother has a piece of it under glass, and a bronze model on the mantel in our city home."

"You have seen the Queen's barge, then," said the Viking softly. "I helped row it once in Oslofjord, and many is the warm afternoon Sigrid of Laagen has ridden in it with King Haakon's bride. But my sword, little kinswoman! My sword! Get it for me now, and let us seal our bond of kinship with that cousinly service."

Karen looked unhappy.

"I am very sorry, cousin Thorbjorn," she said in a troubled voice. "I don't quite know what to do about that. My father has a friend here whom he wants to see it. He is not sure it is ours to give or take. He says the Canadian Government must be consulted in the matter, too."

The Viking's eyes had grown steely.

"I have nothing to do with your father or the Canadian Government," he said angrily. "This lies between you and me alone. You are my kinswoman and the kinswoman of Sigrid of Laagen."

"He," said Karen, simply but firmly, "is my father, and, once we cross the bridge from Buffalo, we Desmonds are the guests of the Canadian Government. But tell me, cousin Thorbjorn. You are a strong man. Since you knew where it was, why did you not take the sword yourself from beneath the oak tree?"

The Viking shuddered.

"The Indian who struck me down from behind," he said, opening and clenching his fist in a passion of anger, "was an evil Shaman. He placed a spell upon my sword. Great is the power of cold iron, and of oak and ash and thorn. Even greater is the power of the Shaman's song over such of us as have passed the cold portal of earth. But it cannot bind innocent little mortal maidens like yourself and your two sisters. You do not have to fear cold iron's ban. I cannot even touch my own good blade's cold iron unless, first, you tender it to me freely, without duress, hilt foremost, you holding it by the smiting blade. That breaks the *geis* the Shaman laid upon it. Will you do that for me, Karen Desmond? We have been separated, I and my sword, all too long."

Karen's eyes were wet.

"Do not be unhappy, cousin Thorbjorn," she soothed him. "I shall do my best."

The Viking smote his gauntlet on the boulder, as if a thought had struck him.

"Tell me, little kinswoman," he said eagerly. "You have pictures of Orkedal? It has been so many, many years since I have seen my valley."

Karen thought a moment.

"No pictures, no," she said shyly. "But Dr. Krehan brought some dolls as presents. I'll only be a minute getting them."

The dolls were still in their tissue-lined boxes in the dining room. Behind the glass French doors, in the living room, a hum of voices rose from around the fireplace where Professor Desmond was showing his guest the sword. Karen slipped the screen catch very quietly and went back again into the silver night. The bell buoy clanged twice as she reached the boulder.

"Aye," said the Viking tenderly. "Some things do not change so fast as others. So they dressed in Orkedal, and in my day. So, it seems, the maids dress still. We will set the moppets here on the rock, little kinswoman. They will make the long night less lonely, and I will do them no scathe."

That night Sigrid of the silver arm band came again to Karen as she slept. This time they stood together on the lake shore. Far out were the shining round heads of seals. One of the sea things swam rapidly to shore, and, as he drew near, Karen noticed with curious distaste — for she liked the sportive beasts — that this one had a man's face. "Careful, little kinswoman!" whispered Sigrid of Laagen.

Early next morning, before Moira and Sheila woke up, Karen recovered the dolls. Their dresses were perfectly dry. But a little dew still rested on the flaxen curls of the Norwegian and Danish dolls, and on the raven-dark hair of the little Lapp girl. Or, wondered Karen with a sinking heart, could it have been tears?

She looked up from the Council Rock back toward the little house huddled into the ground under the early morning light. Everything looked unchanged. She felt unchanged herself. Yet everything had somehow changed. For a time, at least, the gods and heroes walked again among men.

CHAPTER NINE

The Coming of the Indians

WHEN, an hour later, Karen came down the stairs to breakfast, Professor Desmond had a fire roaring like a golden dragon in the gray stone hearth. Mr. Sillerton Jackson sat in front of it on his favorite hassock, kneading the upholstery with his claws — or rather, as the children of the Desmond household preferred to say, "making cat bread." The kitchen was already fragrant with the smell of crisping bacon and what the family had gotten in the habit of calling "beach toast," because it did not pop out of some effete citified toaster but was grilled over one of the driftwood-blue fire circles on the open gas range. Dr. Krehan had not come down yet. Professor Desmond and Mother were sitting at the kitchen table. Father's eyebrows arched when he saw Karen.

"Aha!" he said. "Her Majesty Elizabeth!"

Professor Desmond always called Karen Queen Elizabeth — Shakespeare's Elizabeth, that is — whenever she wore his heavy old white athletic sweater with the pulled up collar that, framing her red ringlets, looked quite a bit like a ruff. He wasn't altogether fooling, either, for Karen had once heard him speak of it to Mother when he didn't know she was listening.

"Funny thing about red hair," he had said. "It's comical or else it's regal. One looks either a Clown or a Queen. Karen looks a Queen. Bozo looks a Clown."

Then her parents went back to their conversation. What bothered Professor Desmond at the moment was a noise he had heard in

148

the night. At first he had thought it was a motorboat. But, when he listened more closely, the noise appeared to have a different timbre than that of a motorboat's. For one thing, the throb was more powerful. So he got out of bed there in the downstairs bedroom he shared with his wife, walked upstairs and looked out on the lake from the bathroom casement window. The moon had set. It was dark as pitch outside in the September night. No, by Jupiter, it wasn't! Not quite. There was a kind of dying glow over near the old pier where the draught was deep enough to moor a yacht and from which point one had to swim at least one hundred yards before being able to set down foot on sand. The dull light was no moon glint, either. It was almost as if a flare were dying away. Then suddenly, whatever the light's origin, it went out altogether. Once again the darkness was total, except for the faint red burnish of the Lackawanna furnaces across the lake and the strange pale luminousness that always invested large bodies of water. Nothing moved. He could catch no sound now. It was only when he was back in bed and half asleep again that he heard the motor's roar a second time. This time there seemed to be no effort to conceal the sound.

Professor Desmond told all this to Mother at the breakfast table. Despite her apprehensions of the day before, Mrs. Desmond poohpoohed his unformulated fears.

"Oh, John," said Mrs. Desmond. "Don't go all over romanticist on me now. The F.B.I. always checks on things like that."

"Oh, does it?" said Professor Desmond, irritated. "Who was all over romanticist yesterday? And, for your information, this happens to be Canada where the F.B.I. has no jurisdiction. Also, if you can remember back to a previous conversation of ours, the F.B.I. keeps no tabs on Krehan anyway. I tell you, Toby, I've got the wind up a little. I really think I ought to notify the Buffalo office of the F.B.I. and let them take it up with the Canadian authorities. If this were Toronto, I'd certainly speak to the local constabulary, too."

"Well, why don't you do it then?" said Mrs. Desmond who was not to be drawn into further discussion.

"By George, I will!" said Professor Desmond.

But, as it turned out, he didn't. Once he had gained his point,

Professor Desmond had a habit of forgetting all about it. Also, like a goodly number of his fellow citizens, he had a holy horror of being tabulated as a boy who cried wolf. Nevertheless, he walked along the almost deserted beach, counted the few boats that were still in their hoists, and satisfied himself that, whatever the noise may have been, it had not been caused by any of the boats belonging to the crescent.

Karen had her own problem. She didn't quite know what to do about the Viking. While eating breakfast, she decided that she had to tell Father eventually, of course, and the sooner the better. But childhood is a secret, if not a silent country, and Karen was still close enough to the primordial borders, where animals talked and trees were persons, to want to keep the elusive laws of that far frontier. Add to this the fact that, as an adolescent, she did not exactly court ridicule at the clumsy hands of the Olympians. Professor Desmond was usually kindly, it was true; but even the most understanding adult's jack boots could be cruelly heavy on the garden of youth. Over her last slice of beach toast, she reached the conclusion that she would have to get her father alone. That, without making too obvious an issue of it, was going to be a hard thing today. Right now she could hear their guest stirring overhead. Mrs. Desmond heard him, too.

"Oh, Karen," she said. "Will you stop by Alec's for two more pounds of pea meal bacon?"

There were two ways to get to Alec Szabo's store. Usually Karen preferred to go by the back road, because it was much quicker and there were always so many other things to do. Today, however, she went by the beach, because the day was so unbelievably beautiful and because, very likely, this would be their last week end of the season. The sky was almost cloudless. Only here and there, white wisps hazed the clear blue. The lake stood still as a mirror except where a chub, mouthing close to the surface, made a momentary circlet of ripple, like a princess' crown in a fairy tale, that at once smoothed into glass again. Whenever this happened, two gulls, which had been rocking on the groundswell that lifted the Mallard raft, took off from the raft, crying like winged white cats, and circled the spot. Karen watched them stoop and strike and carry off their silver-scaled plunder. Something about their royal plumage and their proud carriage in flight made her think of the Sea King and his sword. Red hair blowing across her blue eyes, she said over to herself some lines by Stevenson about the crying curlews, and Melville's little poem about the gull on the spar of the wrecked ship. The gull who kept keening: *The crew? The crew?*

Some driftwood had washed up during the night. Karen made a note of its position. Later on she, Moira, Sheila, and Kristin, who happened to be extraordinarily adept at wood gathering, would stack it for the woodpile in the cellar. It didn't burn so hot or so long as cherry wood, but it gave off much nicer colors. Sheila had named them "witch colors," and Professor Desmond said Samuel Taylor Coleridge couldn't have done any better than that.

Floating quietly beyond the last stick of witch wood was a strip of something white. The Elephant's Child in Karen won out over the grown-up fourteen-year-old. She took off her sandals and waded out to her knees in the ice-cold water. Her booty proved somewhat disappointing. It was only a piece of silk with letters on it. Odd letters. Something like the Greek capitals Professor Desmond liked to draw in the sand for them when he wasn't drawing monkeys, his other specialty. But surely not worth the trouble she had taken. Disappointed, Karen stuffed the wet strip in her pocket, and went on past the Schmidts, the Corrigans, the Kowalskis, the Tedescos, until she reached the road that ran down into the lake and divided the public from the private beach.

It was then she saw the stranger for the first time. Or, rather, saw the back of his head. It was sleek and round and dark like the head of a seal. Even at a distance, Karen felt repulsed. She liked seals, to be sure, but not men who looked like seals. The seal head was bent over a small hole in the ground. Again the Elephant's Child awoke. What was this stranger, who looked like a seal, up to, anyway? Grown men, unless it was Uncle Charlie helping the Desmond children search for treasure, did not dig in the sand. Besides, the stranger seemed to be burying something rather than digging something up. Now he set aside the little spade he had been using and started to tamp down the wet sand with his feet. Suddenly Karen remembered her dream of the seal man and what Sigrid of Laagen had whispered: "Careful, little kinswoman!" Very quietly she walked behind the Scotts' great poplar.

And none too soon. The stranger straightened up and turned toward her. He was of middle height and very tanned. Seen from the front he did not look quite so much like a seal except that his eyes were as cold and expressionless as the eyes of any sea thing. Karen did not like those eyes. They made her feel somehow sickish, even as the eyes of the Viking made her feel warm and good.

The stranger wore dark trousers and a leather jacket. Somehow there was something foreign in the way his shoulders sloped, and in the way he stood. Not nice foreign like Alec, who had been born in Hungary; or like the Ukrainian lady who, once a week, cleaned their city house. Alec and Marya were comfortable at-home foreign. The seal man had a not-at-home foreign air, with much contempt in it. One could tell he felt a fierce superiority to everything about him. As she watched, he lit a cigarette and squatted down looking out to sea. The foreign impression was strengthened by the way he flicked his cigarette ash.

Karen drew a careful bead from the Scotts' poplar to the place where the stranger had buried something. He couldn't have dug very deep with the small spade she had seen him use. After lunch — supposing he had gone by then — it would be easy for her and Moira to dig it up, while Sheila kept watch for them. After that, Karen went on to Alec's store, walking silent in the soft sand and looking back over her shoulder till the bend in the road had hidden the stranger from her sight. He never moved. On her way home from Alec's, she was careful to take the back road.

"Well," said Mrs. Desmond reproachfully as Karen finally came in the screen door, "you've certainly taken your time. If it weren't for that blessed sword, I don't know what we'd have done. As it is, I'm warming up the coffee for the third time, and those men are still around the fire place, talking away. Men will be men, I guess. And professors even more so."

Dr. Krehan was gesturing with an unlighted cigar toward Sheila's blackboard on which he had drawn a sort of diagram map.

"See, John," he said. "It is all intrinsically quite probable as well as possible. The sagas record eleventh-century voyages to the eastern coast of what is now the United States. There were probably others, too. Leif Ericsson's Vinland was almost certainly Massachusetts. He had previously made landings in both Newfoundland and

Nova Scotia. Spears, axes, and one sword of the period have been discovered in Minnesota. Another sword was dug up in northern Ontario and, almost in a direct line with it, an ax in northern Michigan. Whether one is coming up from Massachusetts and Nova Scotia, or down from Newfoundland, Lake Erie is closer to the place of the original landings than any other place in Ontario, or any place at all in either Michigan or Minnesota. I tell you, John, it is more than possible. It all fits."

Of course, it fits, thought Karen to herself. How dull maps and diagrams and professors could be! She wished she could tell Father about the Viking this very minute. But it was hardly the time. Dr. Krehan caught her eye and winked at her. Karen smiled primly back.

"Now let me speak as an amateur anthropologist, John," said Dr. Krehan, beginning his cigar waving all over again. "I started as an anthropologist, you know, before turning to physical chemistry."

"You Germans seem to try everything," said Professor Desmond, interrupting him.

"Almost everything," said Dr. Krehan. "Speaking as an anthropologist, then, I seem to remember a blond and blue-eyed Indian tribe somewhere in the Dakotas."

"Yes," said Professor Desmond. "The Mandans."

"The Mandans," repeated Dr. Krehan, nodding his head. "Yes, the Mandans. They worshiped a great canoe in which, they said, white gods had come to them. It may well have been a dragon ship. Then there was the Frenchman, Champlain. He found a tradition of *mistigoche*, of 'wooden boat men,' among the Iroquois. That would strike even closer to home, would it not? What do you say, Miss Karen?"

Karen was spared the necessity of answering by the arrival of Mother with a most resolute look in her eye.

"I say, gentlemen," announced Mrs. Desmond, "and for the fourteenth and last time, that breakfast is served."

While Professor Desmond ate a second breakfast with Dr. Krehan, Karen walked out on the verandah. In the steamer channel between her and the American shore long freighters were passing out of Buffalo harbor on their way up the Great Lakes. There was a pleasant clink of hammer on metal down where the Brown boys, hip deep in the cold water, were dismantling their motorboat mooring-sling

for the winter. They waved to her. Two houses to the right of the
Desmonds, Mr. Spencer, pipe in mouth, was sandpapering his
boat keel prior to storing it in the garage till spring. He, too, waved
to Karen.

Moira and Sheila were helping Kristin in her eternal task of
digging sand holes and filling them with water. Remembering
what she had seen the stranger burying, Karen thought she knew a
sand game worth ten of theirs. So, when she explained the project
to them, did Sheila and Moira. They were careful to send Kristin
up to the house first. Then they carried down from the wall the
light yellow rubber boat with the blue aluminum sculls that had
once been general issue for flyers in the North Atlantic and South
Pacific and that now provided the best of beach toys for young
American children. Karen expounded her plan before the three
of them pushed off. They would lay to just off the Scotts' great
poplar. If the stranger had gone, well and good. They would there-
upon row ashore and dig up, as rapidly as possible, whatever it was
that he had hidden. If, on the other hand, he was still there, they
would row down as far as Waverly, just around the next point, and
come back hugging the shore. If, on their return, he had not yet left,
they would beach the boat in front of their own cottage, and resume
the attempt that afternoon.

"But this afternoon," said Sheila plaintively, "Daddy's taking me
to the Military Tattoo."

The Military Tattoo was an annual competition for the honor
bands of the frontier area. The Welland Highlanders were scheduled
to march. So was a detachment of Marines from Buffalo and a troop
of Royal Mounted Police from Toronto. The winner was to receive
the Lady Saltoun Cup which Sheila and Moira had seen displayed,
in all its argent glory, in the Adam, Meldrum, and Anderson store
window. It was all very colorful and exciting, so, very naturally, Moira
wanted to go as well. Moira favored the Marines. Sheila, who still,
despite her age, maintained a kind of guilty, unconfessed allegiance
to a Toronto radio station's Kindergarten of the Air, preferred
the Mounties.

"This evening, then," said Karen agreeably.

As it happened, the stranger was still there when they hove to,
feathering the dripping oars in the glassy water some twenty-five

yards or so off the Scotts' huge poplar. Very disagreeably there, too. He was tickling a toad which he had stretched on its back so that it lay kicking, white belly helplessly exposed to the sun. The nasty trick made Sheila, especially, very indignant.

The stranger grinned at the three girls as they lay off shore watching him.

"Hello," he said, showing two even rows of strong white teeth.

Only it sounded to Karen more like "Allo." Later, though, she had to admit that his English had been very, very good. If anything, too good. In fact, a bit too much like a play actor's really to ring true — unless, of course, one was English like Alistair Savage who called roller coasters switchback railways and merry-go-rounds carrousels, and of whose accent the three older Desmond girls were somewhat envious. But Karen was ready to wager her entire collection of that season's sheet music that the stranger was neither English nor American. Nor Canadian, either.

"Hello," said Karen guardedly in return.

"You come from Buffalo, young ladies?" he asked, gesturing to where the great white grain elevators showed, like honeycombs standing on end or else like giant Pan's Pipes, against the Buffalo sky line.

The three girls nodded, without saying anything.

"A nice city, Buffalo," said the stranger, still grinning. "They made the *Cobrushkas* there."

"What are *Cobrushkas*?" Moira asked him, wrinkling her nose, as she always did when thinking.

It had been a slip. But the stranger decided to brazen it out. After all, they were only children.

"What are *Cobrushkas*, little girl?" asked the stranger. "Why, little cobras, little deadly snakes. But you are too young to remember. Perhaps too young to have known. Americans forget so easily that war was, and find it so hard to believe that war ever will be again."

"Cobras come from India," said Moira doubtfully. "They are 'normous snakes with poisoned fangs. Mr. Yeddanapalli told me."

"So they are," said the stranger, and all three girls knew he was mocking them, mocking them hatefully. "Very poisonous fangs indeed. And now, my little friends, I am hungry. With your permission

I shall take myself to a restaurant if, of course, the bourgeois culture of the neighborhood supports so pleasant a thing as a restaurant."

"*Steaks n' Shakes* is a mile down the Dominion Highway," Karen told him politely.

"*Steaks n' Shakes*," said the stranger, bowing. "How unutterably quaint!"

As the stranger got up to go, he brought one heavy square-toed shoe down on the struggling toad. It was no accident. The girls' boat had drifted inshore far enough for them to see the whole thing clearly and also to hear the shrill bleating tiny squeal of the tormented thing.

"My word," said the seal man, grinning more hatefully than ever. "What a horrid creature!"

Without a backward glance at the children, he set off walking up the cut to the back road. Sheila, of course, was all for making for the beach at once to see if she could help the stricken toad in any way. But her prudent oldest sister insisted on sculling out another fifty yards in order to keep the stranger in sight. The precaution was wise but unnecessary. He kept on walking until he reached the back road. Then turned and went out of sight. With quick, sure strokes Karen pulled for the shore.

By now the maimed creature was well beyond any assistance. The golden eyes had paled. The pulsing throat and quivering stomach were still. After one swift look Karen dispatched Sheila, now more indignant than ever, to stand watch from the crotch of Scotts' poplar whence one could rake the beach road for half a mile in any direction. Quickly the two older girls set to digging. The stranger had had very little time for what he had to do. A shallow trench was soon uncovered. In it lay what appeared to be a heavy, sodden mass of silk with tangled cords attached to it. Without pausing to examine it closely, they set the messy thing in the boat; then fell to filling up the trench again. Not till the sand was neatly tamped down all around once more, was scout Sheila recalled from her post and the three set off again. They beached their light boat expertly, carried it up to their own porch, and then sat down, under the sheltered lee of the retaining wall, to examine the find. Moira didn't think it much at all.

"It's just an old wet thing," she said, disgusted. "Why would anyone want to bury an old wet thing like this?"

"That," said Karen, poring over the rumpled silk, "is just the point. It's like Sherlock Holmes and the dog in the night time."

"What about Sherlock Holmes and the dog in the night time?" asked Moira.

"Sherlock," said Karen, by way of explanation, "said something to Watson about the strange incident of the dog in the night time, and when Watson said that he hadn't heard any dog in the night time, Sherlock said: 'Exactly. That is what I refer to as the strange incident of the dog in the night time.' At least, that's as close as I can remember it."

"I don't get it," said Sheila. "But I think I know why he buried the old thing. It's because he's a bad man."

"That's for sure," said Moira.

One thing checked anyway. The piece of material matched up with the strip in Karen's pocket even to continuing the odd Greek capitals. She was putting the two strips together like a cloth jigsaw puzzle when Billy Brown, who lived next door and who had been with the PT boats in the South Pacific, looked over the wall.

"Hi, kids," he said. "What are you doing with the parachute?"

"Nothing," said Karen, more pieces of the puzzle clicking into place in her mind.

Children forgot fast, and, by any count, the World War II years belonged to Karen's early childhood. Nevertheless, she remembered now what a Cobra was — an airplane manufactured during the war in the Bell Plant between Buffalo and Niagara Falls. Her father had done some industrial journalism in the interests of that plane which had been exported, via the Archangel route, in great numbers to beleaguered Russia. She also remembered what her father had said that morning about calling the F.B.I. And she recalled, with peculiar vividness, her dream of the seal man and how Sigrid of Laagen had whispered a warning against him. It was time to talk to her father. But once again it proved impossible to get Father alone. Till Mother called them for lunch, he and Dr. Krehan played three dimensional chess on an eight storied little skyscraper whose floors were transparent glass marked off in squares. Dr. Krehan had brought the elaborate game with him from Washington. It had no less than sixty-four chessmen, including, in addition to the usual medieval figures, such new and appropriate pieces as space knights, hippogriffs, and jesters. To match, Dr. Krehan told Professor Desmond with a chuckle, the changed complexion of international politics which preserved intact all the old follies and added some new ones all its own.

That afternoon, while Sheila and Moira went to the Military Tattoo with Professor Desmond, Karen curled up in the sand-warmed lee of the wall and thought, *The Complete Sherlock Holmes* lying unopened on her lap. Mother sat on the porch and sewed. Dr. Krehan strolled down the beach. He had heard enough military bands in his day, he told Professor Desmond. Karen managed to keep him in view at all times. Her heart missed a beat once as he passed the Scotts' poplar. But nothing happened. No one was in sight the length and breadth of the beach; and, after pacing off an equal distance in the opposite direction, Dr. Krehan joined Mother on the porch. Later on in the afternoon, as the sun began to descend the western slope, the seal man turned up once more. He had binoculars now which, once or twice, he trained on the Desmond house. But only once or twice, and he trained them on many other subjects as well. Most of the time he simply sat well back from the water's edge against the Scotts' wall, smoking numerous cigarettes, and always making sure he could not be seen from the verandahs in the center of the crescent.

By evening Karen had read half of *The Adventure of the Blue Carbuncle*, and had resolved on two things. She would speak to Father about the Viking before nightfall; as soon, in fact, as he came back from the Tattoo. And she would ask him about the F.B.I. There was no chance to do either before dinner. As it turned out, aggravatingly, Sheila kept going on about her favorite Mounties who had carried off the Lady Saltoun Cup. After dinner, was even worse. As the minutes ticked away, Karen began to dread her dual task. She could see that the Viking matter was going to take a tall bit of explaining — even for the most understanding of fathers who, what with his guest and what with the sword, never seemed unoccupied even for a minute. She did manage, however, to catch him alone for a bare second as he rolled up the porch side awning for the night.

"I think," Karen said, "you told Mother this morning you wanted to call Buffalo today."

Professor Desmond looked at her sharply. He wondered what was going on behind the candid blue eyes so like his own.

"Yes, I did," he said quizzically. "Want to walk to Szabo's with me?"

One of the Desmonds' professorial economies was no beach telephone. There was one next door at the Browns', who happened to be a Doctor's family, but they had locked up and driven in to Buffalo at 5:30 that afternoon. As chance or fate or providence would have it, the usually provident Mr. Szabo, who had a pay telephone in his store, had closed up shop early, for once. No one answered Professor Desmond's impatient knock at either front or back door. It was a pity, as it turned out later. A pity, too, that Professor Desmond had not driven the five miles or so to a drug store phone, as he had been more than half minded to. Or was it? Afterward Karen could never decide. Perhaps, as the favorite Arabian tales of her childhood liked to put it, it had all been written. Written in the stars. At all events, if Mr. Szabo had not gone into Ridgeway or Fort Erie or Port Colborne, or wherever it was he went that Saturday night at the end of September, the Viking would not have gotten his sword back.

As, in the fast gathering early autumn darkness, they turned in to their own driveway, Professor Desmond put a hand on his daughter's shoulder.

"I don't know what's going on under that red thatch of yours," he said meaningly, "but I should like you to know the name of the man I was going to call. And also his number. His name is Mr. Christopher Conboy of the Federal Bureau of Investigation. His number is Mohawk 7800. Now repeat that after me."

"Mr. Christopher Conboy of the Federal Bureau of Investigation," said Karen obediently. "At Mohawk 7800. I'll write them down as soon as we get inside."

"O.K.," said Professor Desmond, kissing her. "And don't forget it."

It was to prove a valuable piece of information, even if, when it came to the test, Karen had not been able to bring herself to tell her father about the Viking. Why had she not been able? she asked herself afterward many times without reaching any conclusion. She could not know that there was no answer to such a question. The deepest questions had no answers. A boy's will was the wind's will; a girl's will was earth's and the silence of earth. Some things one did not talk about — not even to a father.

The evening had disclosed one more valuable piece of information. Sheila met the chocolate turtle man again. It was while Karen and Professor Desmond were on the way to Szabo's. Mother sent Sheila, who was the most reliable of her daughters in this particular respect, down to the wall to pick up Kristin's sand toys. When the child moved to the left of the wall's base, there, in a hidden coign of vantage formed by the Browns' wall running out beyond the Desmonds', sat their stranger of the morning. Beside him, back curved uncomfortably against the rough cold masonry, was the little man she had seen twice before — once looking out over the Severn and once in front of the *Cosmos Club*. The child jumped. But, as usual, her aplomb was sufficient.

"Hello," she said uncertainly.

"Allo," said the stranger sullenly.

"Not you," said Sheila. "Him."

She pointed at Mr. Tikjan. Mr. Tikjan squirmed a little.

"Hello," he said.

When the child had gone back to the house, the stranger turned to Mr. Tikjan.

"That is one of the children with whom Krehan is staying?"

"Yes," said Mr. Tikjan. "The identification is made. You know the house now. My job is done."

"She seems to know you, Comrade Tikjan," said the stranger, showing his teeth in a grin, and mentally recording the irritating fact that he could just as easily have made the identification himself without the intervention of this little bungler.

"Oh, not that, Comrade," said Mr. Tikjan, uneasily deprecating the suggestion. "I believe, however, that she did notice me once, standing outside the *Cosmos Club* in Washington where Dr. Krehan lives. Do not concern yourself. It is nothing important."

Mr. Tikjan did not think it necessary to mention the Annapolis camera incident to this high-ranking Comrade from Outside. His intuition was correct, so far as it went. In the final event, it did not make any difference. The Comrade from Outside had already made up his very efficient mind. The equation was a simple one, really. Mr. Tikjan was expendable. He was not. The child might well put two and two together. *Ergo*, it was expedient that Mr. Tikjan be removed. The Comrade from Outside was a man of decision. He tossed the stub of his cigarette away from the wall.

"Help me get this rubber boat down to the water's edge," he said. "You take the sculls. I'll take the boat. There is something on that pier I must get rid of."

Mr. Tikjan did not care for boats and water. He had also, during a nocturnal coach ride down from Washington, with Dr. Krehan presumably warm and comfortable in a roomette, caught a raging cold in a sensitive antrum. His right jaw was now swollen, both ears and neck glands were involved, and his lower teeth ached to the point where he could not even down the three remaining chocolate turtles in the box in his pocket. But Mr. Tikjan was a man under discipline. He complied.

By the time the two of them reached the pier, it was already pitch dark. The Comrade from Outside helped Mr. Tikjan up the crumbling sides. Four feet below them water lapped coldly all around.

"I do not see anything to be gotten rid of here," said Mr. Tikjan uneasily.

"You don't, Comrade Tikjan?" asked the stranger mockingly.

He had a heavy wrench in his hand now. With a single agile movement, he suddenly hit Mr. Tikjan over the temple. There was a dull cracking noise as if an egg had been opened against a kitchen sink. The man who liked chocolate turtles fell forward slowly on his face. There had been something ritual, almost hieratic in the stranger's action. He had slain dispassionately, wielding the wrench like some high priest using an obsidian knife for sacrifice. He wiped the heavy tool. It was not necessary. Mr. Tikjan had not even bled.

"You, Mr. Tikjan," the stranger said aloud in his own language, "are what I had to get rid of on the pier."

There were loose stones on the old stone dock. Heavy ones. The stranger had marked them the previous night by the light of the flare when the sea plane set him down. He carried strong twine in his pocket. It was the work of only a few minutes to lash certain heavy stones to Mr. Tikjan, and to push him over the edge of the pier. He would eventually come up again, of course, when the twine rotted away. But, with a little luck, not till spring. All the time his killer needed now, at the very outside, was an additional thirty-six hours. And perhaps not even that.

Before rolling the body over the edge, by the light of a pocket flash, cunningly masked, the stranger, who seemed an expert at this unlovely business, rifled Mr. Tikjan's pockets. There was very little in them. A wallet with thirty dollars in single rolled bills in it. The stranger transferred these to his own pocket. A cardboard box with three chocolate turtles still left intact. With a little smile of contempt on his face, the stranger tipped the contents into the water. A folded *Tabloid* newspaper dated the day before. The paper was open to a book remainder sale. The stranger read the list with some interest. It was the usual thing. Art books. The posters of Toulouse-Lautrec. Erotica. He passed over *Torture Garden, Justine, Venus in Furs* — these he already owned — in favor of an interesting looking item he did not happen to possess. *Nell in Bridewell.* "Vigorously illustrated," read the prospectus. His full lips pouted out a little, the Comrade from Outside ripped out the page. It was a mistake, though he would not find that out for some hours. The Comrade from Outside did not care for chocolate turtles. But he did have individual tastes of his own.

The man who liked chocolate turtles had not been a bad little fellow after his fashion. If there was a melancholy lesson in his death by water, it was the banal old one of *facilis descensus Averni. The descent to the abyss is easy.* And that descent moved by geometrical progression. The Comrade from At Home had paved the way for the Comrade from Outside. If there was no other sustenance available, the prime snake could always live by devouring part of itself.

After Kristin had finally crooned herself and Bozo to sleep with an unseasonal *Hark, the Herald Angels Sing,* Karen quietly crept into the girls' bedroom across the hall. Sheila was just finishing her account to Moira of the man who looked like a chocolate turtle of whom she had not spoken at supper. Sheila was not quite so firm a citizen of the secret commonwealth of childhood as her two older sisters, but she had been deterred by other considerations. She remembered Professor Desmond's outburst at Annapolis. It took Karen, who had not been at Annapolis, an extra moment or two to get her bearings in this new development. When she realized the possible significance of the connection between the stranger and his ugly little visitor, the jigsaw puzzle was at last almost complete. Only a small piece, here and there, remained to be inserted.

"And there," Sheila was saying, "beside the bad man sat the — " Sheila groped for a word somewhat embarrassedly.

"Yes," Karen prompted her, "the — go on, Sheila."

"The," said Sheila, smiling defensively now, "the — you know, Karen."

"But I don't know!" said Karen, exasperated.

Moira had fewer linguistic inhibitions.

"She means the jerk who looks like a chocolate turtle," said Moira. "We saw him at Annapolis. Sheila tried to take his picture, but he turned his back."

"And I saw him at the *Cosmos Club* before that," said Sheila, relieved to get over the forbidden hurdle.

So the story got told. When Sheila finished her rather rambling account, Karen finally got down to telling them her part of the story — the part about the Viking, that is. She saw no point in harrowing her younger sisters with suspicions that she had not yet managed to verify. After Karen had finished in her turn, Sheila, with a little sniff, said she thought it was about time she and Moira got to hear of it. Moira didn't say anything at all. She was too busy staring at the upstairs window pane. It was a twenty foot drop to the ground below. But there was a face at the window.

"Is that the Viking, Karen?" Moira asked in the smallest possible voice.

Karen jumped at the sight of the face pressed against the pane. No, it wasn't the Viking. It was, if possible, something even more startling. A dark mask of a face with white lines traced across it, and a single feather a-top the gleaming head.

"Are Vikings Indians, Karen?" asked Sheila in a voice as small as Moira's.

Of course! It was an Indian. And a friendly one, too, despite the war paint, if one could judge from the way he smiled and beckoned to the three girls, as if inviting them to leave their beds and come out. Karen hadn't even time to wonder how he had managed to get up there so close to the chimney when the Viking's face appeared beside the Indian's. Then she knew it was all right for them to accept the Indian's invitation and go out under the clear stars of the early autumn night.

"They want us to come out," said Karen. "I think it's all right to go."

"They?" asked Moira. "I can only see one Indian."

"Of course there's only one Indian," said Karen impatiently. "Thorbjorn's beside him."

"I don't see him," said Moira.

"Neither do I," said Sheila.

We can settle that later, thought Karen to herself. The thing to do now was to get down the stairs as quietly as anything, and out to what she had begun to think of as the Council Rock. So, still as three mice, two little girls and one big girl put on slippers and plaid wool bathrobes, crept down the silent staircase, and through the back screen door out into a night of stars and trees.

As a matter of fact, there were two Indians, not just one, both standing beside the Viking at the Council Rock. One was the brave the three girls had seen at the window. He was tall and straight, a tomahawk in his left hand, a crimson blanket slung over his right shoulder. The other was a slim Indian maid in ivory buckskin soft and clean as new-fallen snow, and a single white feather against the dark night of her hair. Both Indians gravely put out their hands to the children. To Karen first. Then to Moira. And last of all to Sheila.

"My friends, little kinswomen," said the Viking with a flourish. "Great Bear, the warrior. His squaw, White Owl."

Then Thorbjorn, in his turn, put out a large hand to Moira.

"*Skål, lille trold!*" he roared.

But Moira never put out her little hand in answer, and, suddenly, Karen understood why she failed to do so. Sheila and Moira were able to see the Indians perfectly. For some reason that, even afterward, they were unable to decipher, Moira and Sheila could not see the Viking. When Karen explained it to him, Thorbjorn seemed somehow sad.

"Yes, little red one," he said dejectedly. "They, as much as you, are of the blood of Sigrid of Laagen. And still they cannot see. You are the only one from outside to have seen me these nine hundred years and more. It is lonely and cold in the shadow world."

He clutched her fiercely by the arm. She wondered if there would be black and blue marks in the morning.

"That," he said, "is why I must have my sword, and quickly. Get me my sword, Karen Desmond. Then, at last, I can leave these shores of exile."

At that very moment a falling star blazed across the velvet dark like a flaming arrow shot from on high.

"Look!" said Moira, who as late as a year ago had liked to play Robin Hood with toy cross bow and long bow, and who felt more like Robin Hood than ever out here in the dark with all the grown-ups asleep. "Look! It's like an arrow!"

White Owl laughed. Hers was a lovely laugh, the girls were later to agree. Low and musical, like a woodland stream chiming over sunny rocks. She whispered something in her tall husband's ear. It did not exactly become red-skinned braves to laugh. But Great Bear smiled a little. And his eyes were very kind.

"You say these are your kinswomen, my brother Thorbjorn?" said Great Bear in his deep organ tones. "I, too, claim them for my Lodge. At least the little fair one must be mine. Look at her eyes. They are blue, but they have the red man's slant that comes from narrowing to see the track of deer on woodland trails. I claim the little fair one for my own. She must be mine."

"Or mine," said White Owl. "She is of my clan. She is soft and white and pretty as a little snow owl."

Then, diplomatically:

"I claim the little smooth-faced one, too. She is brown and quick as an autumn leaf in the wind. Their Indian names shall be Snow Owl and Oak Leaf."

Another star fell. This time Karen noticed that it sped through the night from somewhere near the seven stars of the Great Dipper.

"The Sky Hunters draw near their quarry," said Great Bear, watching the direction of her gaze. "Know you what we Indians call those stars?"

Great Bear took no liberties with Karen. Thorbjorn had told him certain things. Also, he was a gentleman and could see for himself. He spoke to her, courtly and familiar, as one chief spoke to another.

Karen thought a moment.

"Once I heard Father call them 'wampum of the night,' " she said hesitantly.

Great Bear pondered the figure.

"It is a good word," he said judiciously, "and an Indian one. It would please the Great Spirit. Your father is a poet? Poems are strong medicine."

"Yes," said Karen, "I suppose he could be called a poet. But 'wampum of the night' is not his. He told me it came from a New England lady who wrote almost a century ago."

"Someday," said Great Bear politely, "I should like to hear something of your father's poetry."

"You would?" asked Karen, thrilled. "I don't know quite what it all means, but I can recite one he made this summer."

It was more, very possibly, than Great Bear had bargained for. But Indians were trained courtiers. He and White Owl sat, impassive as bronzed statues, during the recitation. Not so the Viking who frowned and snapped his gauntleted fingers in vexation. Never had he cared for the old skalds who recited while the wine went round King Haakon's board, no, not even for the greatest of them all, skald Egil, son of Skallagrim. Here there was no wine, and for skald only a red-haired New World Irish child who, for a wonder, yet came of his own line, had touched his sword, and still kept the weapon in ward. White Owl smiled a little as she saw the Viking shut his eyes in agony.

"Father," said Karen, stumbling a bit over the unfamiliar French, "calls it: *Aubade au Clair de Lune, Lake Erie.* He says it is a sonnet, but not a perfect one, and this is how it goes.

> *O profitable spendthrift. Lady Night!*
> *To squander all thy small stars' silver store,*
> *Thy argent thrippence and great pieces d'or,*
> *Yet do thy moon-meshed velvet purse no slight,*
> *But plump it tighter than at white midnight,*
> *At morning round, bright, softer-minted, more,*
> *Now Dawn, shy abigail, slides to thy door*
> *And footman Sun awakes the Lord of Light.*

What strange exchange of lune-rune currency!
How changed thou silver Sovereign for gold?
A lucky turn upon the sky's slow wheel?
A sudden cast into the star-rich sea
The Dipper's dice-box from? Or guilder told
Into thy glove for dreams that love-lids seel?"

The clear girl-voice rang brave and moving under the stars of Lady Night. White Owl touched Karen's hand with her own buckskin-fringed one.

"It was very pretty, child," she said.

"I," said the Viking gruffly, "I do not much like poems."

"I like them very much," said Great Bear. "The wind speaks in them and the rain. Now let me tell you what the Indians call those same seven stars."

He looked over at the unhappy Viking.

"It is your sign as well as mine, remember?" he said to Thorbjorn. "We are of one blood, you and I. Thor the Bear, swordman of Sea Kings. Great Bear, bowman of the Iroquois. And yonder is the great Sky Bear and the hunters who follow him with their keen star arrows. See!"

Great Bear feathered an arrow on the bow that had lain unobserved all this time, propped against the Council Rock. The three girls followed the pointing shaft till it came to rest square in the midst of the four stars that formed the Dipper's Box. Slowly, under the deep magic of the Indian's voice and pointing arrow, a gigantic bear seemed to shape itself in the heavens before their very eyes.

"The chase is nearing its end," intoned Great Bear. "The Star Bear grows weary. The three Star Hunters quicken their pace. Look where the first aims his arrow again. See! He lets fly!"

Sure enough, another falling star arched through the sky. Moira waited till the fiery arc had traced its course against the night, then quietly turned back to the house. There was something in a leather pouch beside her bed. Something she had to have. When she stole downstairs again, the something hung around her neck on a leather thong. It was the arrowhead and moonstone Louis Bourdon's wife had given her last fall.

Great Bear was still speaking of the stars and pointing to them.

"The Bear is hurt," he said. "His blood drips now upon the

maple and the sycamore. Tomorrow will their leaves be crimson with his life's blood. Look again where the second Hunter makes ready his bright Star Pot to cook the stricken beast. Look still again where the third Hunter gathers up the Star Fagots for kindling to set beneath the Star Pot."

"We have gone over this matter before," said Thorbjorn angrily. "Which of those seven great stars call you the Star Pot?"

Great Bear pointed to the second star in what the Desmond children had always thought of as the curving handle of the Dipper.

"Not so," said Thorbjorn obstinately. "I told you before and I tell you again, it is the frozen toe of archer Orvandil that Thor flung into the northern skies. Thor is my patron, and the patron of bears. I should know about such things. As for the other stars, they were forged by the frost elves in mine own Northland where the sun shines all the night, and hung up there to be the playthings of the gods."

Great Bear stared broodingly at the Viking. His slanted eyes were narrowing when White Owl tugged at his sleeve, whispered something in his ear, and pointed to the buckskin thong round Moira's neck. The moonstone and arrowhead gleamed in the moonlight. Great Bear looked searchingly at them. He drew in his breath with a hiss.

"Yes," he said aside to White Owl. "You are right. The child is *orenda*. That means that she and hers are under the protection of the Great *Oki*. And she wears the symbols of our tribe besides. Something stirs now in the pool of time. I think we give her the wrong name. She is not Snow Owl. She is Little Star."

Great Bear looked up into the sky again. Fighting was an honorable estate, but it did not do to quarrel idly in the presence of one who bore the mark of *orenda* upon her. He must appease his angry friend and beloved foe. He put one sinewy hand on the Norseman's mailed arm.

"Whether," Great Bear said mildly, "they be gods or only of the gods is probably the same thing in the end. Nine hundred years of argument have not changed the mind of either of us — nor will a second nine. Besides, what can it matter to us, Thor the Bear? To us who are of one blood and share the same totem? White Owl is wiser than we. While we quarrel about nothing for the ten thousandth time, another Hunter is awake in the night skies, and he does not hunt the Bear. There is danger afoot. Great danger. Look!"

By squinting her eyes till they watered, Karen was able to see another Hunter Star moving west in the tail of the Dipper. Thorbjorn's sharper eyes spied it out at once.

"By the thunder of Thor, my brother!" he cried. "You are right and I am a fool! What means this fourth Hunter in the western skies?"

All of a sudden Karen thought she knew.

"Perhaps," she said shyly, "it has something to do with this."

And so the child, who moved yet on the borderlands of life, told her tale at last. But not to her father, nor to the police of her great country. She took the strip of parachute silk from one bathrobe pocket, where she had transferred it after supper, and, while it was passing from hand to hand, told of the coming of the seal man. She did not have to explain what a seal was. Both Indians had been in northern waters more than once, up where the skin kayaks ply to and fro. As for Thorbjorn, he had sighted tens of thousands of the sleek bobbing heads in the days before he made his New World landfall on that last voyage now so many weary centuries in the past. Only once did the listeners halt Karen — when she spoke of the brutal slaying of the toad.

"It was an evil thing," said Great Bear. "I am not of the clan of my brother the Toad — but are not all four-footed things under the protection of *Glooskap*? And was it not the Toad who, when there was nothing in space but water, dived down deep and brought back living earth to the shell of the Great Turtle, and so saved our world? Surely not even the *Pau-Puk-Keewis* — and they are not of the kinder gods — would harm the Toad."

"Aye," said the Viking, growling in his strong throat. "I knew the Paddock folk well in my garden back in Sognefjord. They did no harm to any living creatures except flies. And their eyes were like jewels. It was a foul deed your seal man did. He will do worse. Great Bear, let us try the bones of Divination, you and I."

From the pouch at his belt Great Bear took two polished knucklebones. He scooped a smooth place out in the sand before the Council Rock, breathed on his bones, then cast them.

"Well?" asked Thorbjorn roughly.

The Indian looked up from where the knucklebones lay shining on the moonlit sand. His finger pointed at Karen.

"This one," he said, "is in danger. Great danger. The Hunter hunts for her and for another one I do not know. An older one. One who has something to do with the red child's father, and who stays now in the red child's lodge."

Dr. Krehan, of course. The hair prickled on Karen's head. Sheila and Moira stared at her, wide-eyed. Great Bear replaced the knucklebones in his pouch, and in their stead drew out a gray whetstone on which he then proceeded to sharpen his tomahawk. White Owl tested the strings of her lord's great bow; then ranged his sharp arrows in an orderly row. Humming a little song about a shield wall that made Karen think of swords and shields in battle-clash, Thorbjorn set another helmet on his head. This one, Karen noticed, had no wings, unlike the pictures of Viking helmets in her childhood storybooks, and also unlike the dress helm he had worn last night. It was more businesslike somehow: round iron skullcap with nose and cheek protectors, the metal tip cresting into the figure of a bear. There were pictures of helmets like it in her father's archaeology books. Still humming his song, Thorbjorn led the three girls down the plank walk from the great boulder to the back screen door. Great Bear and White Owl remained, black outlined in the moonlight, against the white of Council Rock.

As the girls went in the door, Thorbjorn patted the head of each one.

"Never fear, little kinswomen," he said to all three, but kissing Karen only, "the Bear warriors watch tonight."

His hand on Karen's head had been cool and firm.To Moira and Sheila, who could not see him, it was like the touch of a poplar leaf falling slowly through the autumn night.

The great dicing presences, who watch the warp and woof of things, had made their cast. The tapestry with the eagle and sickle upon it was almost complete — all except for that last corner where, more and more clearly now, the dragon ship came into shape under the flying fingers. Now Moira and Sheila, too, walked on the marches of myth, were part of myth themselves, yet found nothing strange. Nor was there anything strange to find. It was only when one stood outside of myth that myth seemed strange.

~~~~~~

CHAPTER TEN

The Going of the Viking

SUNDAY began next morning, like every other beach Sunday, to the pleasant tune of bubbling coffee pot and pea meal bacon hissing in the frying pan. Then came the frantic search for hats which, because of St. Paul's misogyny, Professor Desmond used to say, even little women had to wear in church. It relieved Karen's mind a good deal to hear that Dr. Krehan intended to ride along with them. He would wait outside, smoking, until the service was over. Then Mother and the children were to take the Dominion bus back to Crescent Beach, while Father and Dr. Krehan crossed the Peace Bridge into Buffalo and motored inland to the Cattaraugus Reservation where Father wanted Dr. Krehan to talk to an old Indian he knew. It all had something to do with the sword on the mantel, and with Professor Desmond's trip last fall to Christian Island.

"I tell you," said Professor Desmond, filling his pipe while Dr. Krehan took down the sword for what must have been the hundredth time, "it's another piece of evidence. Call it romantic folklore, if you will, but why should a *Grettissaga* analogue turn up on a Cattaraugus reservation in the form of a crude fairy tale told by an old Indian? And why should the same story still be alive among the Indians of Georgian Bay? The Indiana folklore people tell me that the Mandans also had the tale, and that it has been recorded among the Blackfeet who once had a settlement near the site of the Kensington rune-stone find."

"*Ja, ja,* John," said Dr. Krehan, smiling broadly. "I have no objec-

171

tion to meeting your old Indian. It will have a sentimental value for me, you know. Why, when I was a boy, we always played at Cowboys and Indians, not at Vikings, as you seem to have done. After all, what were the Vikings in the last analysis but tenth-century Nazis?"

"I never played at Vikings," said Professor Desmond, a little miffed, putting the sword back on the mantel. "And, what is more, I'm not playing now."

A piping wind was sending breakers crashing over the Niagara River granite breakwall, as Professor Desmond parked his Chevrolet outside the little white-walled Catholic church on the Garrison Road some three miles from Crescent Beach. The air was so clear today that downtown Buffalo stood out in stereopticon relief. One felt one had only to reach out a hand across the swift-flowing Niagara and pick up the city as if it were a colored post card view in a drugstore window. Even the colors had that same vivid implausibility. A few white clouds huddled, like sheep, against the rush of September air. Gulls, blown inland, circled the churchyard headstones with their ceaseless, passionless cat's mewing. Dr. Krehan propped himself against the low church wall and, for once, took out a cigarette instead of a cigar.

"Don't worry about me," he said comfortably. "I will smoke an end-of-summer fag and discuss the transcendental with myself. It will be a change from folklore."

"And from world affairs," said Professor Desmond, a bit irritably. He was always a little irritable when he had to move the children on schedule.

"Yes, John," agreed Dr. Krehan. "From world affairs, too. No politics on Sunday."

As the Desmonds went in the church door, Moira gave Karen's hand a secret squeeze.

"See, Karen," she said, pointing to the crimsoning maples. "See how red they are. Like the Indian said."

Professor Desmond brought up the rear of the little procession with Kristin and that sacerdotal stowaway, Bozo Belinda. He stopped short when he saw Bozo.

"Hey," he said. "What's Bozo doing here?"

"Bozo's a big boy now," said Kristin. "He's in second year college."

"Is he?" said Professor Desmond sardonically. "He must be super-Clown. He was only in third year high school last week."

"Bozo's not a clown," said Kristin firmly. "He only looks like a clown."

"O.K.," said Professor Desmond. "I accept your subtle distinction. Even so, leave him outside."

"I'll take him, John," called Dr. Krehan from his post by the church wall.

Professor Desmond tossed him the battered doll. Dr. Krehan caught it by the left leg and propped it beside him while he smoked. It was odd how living a person the smallest Desmond child had managed to make out of the grotesque toy. Why, Bozo was more alive than the homunculus in *The Cabinet of Dr. Caligari*. Or was it so odd, after all? From their earliest beginnings, men were all creators at heart. He could remember a tiny lead grenadier of his own, and the campaigns it had fought up and down the walks of the *Tiergarten*.

Dr. Krehan turned his attention from the doll to the Desmonds. They were a good family. His old friend, John, had chosen well. Though he would have scorned it once, he liked this habit of Sunday church, for example, and the fact that the three older girls had foregone breakfast in order to receive the Sacrament. The ritual had an ancient dignity. It set up a desirable pattern within the psyche. If, on the Pascalian principle, it corresponded to anything objective in the order of reality, so much the better. If it meant nothing, what harm? On balance, he began to incline to the opinion that it meant something, after all.

While, outside in the churchyard, Dr. Krehan thought on sacred things, inside, in the stuccoed church, like Martha a harried Karen was busy with more mundane matters. She found herself going over timetables during the sermon. She had decided by now that, whatever the knucklebones had to say about it, the seal man was much more likely looking for Dr. Krehan first and for herself second, if at all. There was her father's uneasiness, to add to her own. His references to Mother about Dr. Krehan's political importance. His having her memorize the phone number of the Buffalo Office of the Federal Bureau of Investigation, and the name of an agent he knew.

Mentally she added up the hours it would take to drive to the Cattaraugus Reservation and back. Two and a half hours each way. Two hours there. An hour and a half for dinner in Buffalo. That made eight and a half hours — say nine at the outside, allowing for Sunday traffic. That would have them returning between eight-thirty and nine in the evening; and by then it would already have been dark for a little while. Darkness was the area of real danger. But things should be safe until then. And, with the coming of dark, came also her friends, the Bear warriors, Thorbjorn and his Indian brother. Should she speak to her father now in front of Dr. Krehan? It would be her last chance. Again the unaccountable reluctance overtook her.

When the family came out of the little church, Dr. Krehan seemed to be in a most expansive mood. He gestured toward the little graveyard.

"I was just saying to myself," he told Professor Desmond, "that I envy the quiet citizens of this grassy republic. Judging from their headstones, they have no history but a private one. The only death in war occurred in 1812. You could not find such a cemetery in Europe any more — not even in Switzerland. But please pardon me. I fall into one of the two great German vices, of which the other one is war. In other words I wax pedantically sentimental. Eh, Kristin? What is your philosophy of old mortality?"

Kristin, already repossessed of Bozo, pointed to a noseless, weather-beaten angel striking a pre-Raphaelite pose over one frost-heaved tombstone.

"There's an angel buried there," she stated categorically.

Dr. Krehan laughed.

"A logical but false deduction," he said gaily. "By the same token, Kristin, what would you say is buried here?"

Kristin looked at the battered lamb couchant on a tiny stone.

"A little sheep," she said with similar decisiveness.

"Equally logical," said Dr. Krehan. "And equally false. There, John, you have a vivid demonstration of the limits of reason."

There was a saturnine look on Professor Desmond's face as he digested his colleague's jubilant antirationalism. He was just pondering the retort mordant, when Sheila came up with one of her usual brightly amiable *non sequiturs*.

"Did you notice," she said to Moira, "that all the altar boys were dark-haired at that Mass?"

"No," said Moira, affronted.

"And there," said Professor Desmond, abandoning his prepared epigram, and making a hopeless gesture, "there you have the disadvantages of the statistical method."

"Or," said Mrs. Desmond swiftly, "the advantages."

Dr. Krehan was still laughing to himself when Professor Desmond put Mrs. Desmond and the four girls down at the Peace Bridge Bus stop. Sometimes, Karen thought to herself, a grownup's sense of humor was the most unaccountable thing. There was another reason for her irritation. The last chance to speak out — before evening, at least — had come and gone. She had not spoken; and she felt more than a little guilty and worried about it.

Twice during that endless afternoon Karen scouted the Scotts' great poplar. There was no sign of the seal man anywhere. On her third trip, just after supper — it must have been 7:30, and already the dusk had gray-steeled the lake — he was still nowhere to be seen. But a cigarette butt smoldered near the water's edge. Without quickening her pace, Karen walked past it one hundred yards to a point opposite the old pier, and then, every bit as leisurely, retraced her steps. Not till she was back on her own front porch once more, did the child look around the way she had just come. It was growing a little hard to see now. But the seal man was back at his old post all right, wearing a leather jacket against the evening cold, and training his binoculars on the steamer channel. As she watched he slipped them into his pocket again, took out another cigarette, and sat down to wait. The seal man was very patient.

Karen's calculations were not far off. Precisely at 8:30 the green family Chevrolet drove into the black-topped parking space behind the house. The two men seemed quite excited over the results of their afternoon drive. So excited in fact that they almost forgot to compliment Mrs. Desmond on her excellent Scandinavian meat sauce. Professor Desmond even went so far as to take the sword off the mantel and set it in the middle of the supper table as a centerpiece, first hefting it himself, and then insisting that Dr. Krehan heft it, too.

"Ach, John," said Dr. Krehan. "How impatient you have been all evening to get back to your sword! I thought only we Germans were possessed of the *mystique* of the sword. We and the Japanese."

"Not at all," said Professor Desmond. "The French have their rapiers and the English their cutlasses. I think the sword must be one of Jung's archetypes. But seriously, Gottfried, what did you think of our afternoon's evidence?"

"Most impressive, my friend," said Dr. Krehan soberly. "Most impressive as well as most suggestive. All joking aside, I think you are working on a very tenable hypothesis. Even the parapsychological manifestations, coming as forerunners, seem significant — the trance in the amusement park, for example. Did you know, by the bye, that it was *séance* evidence that first pointed the way to the Sutton Hoo grave mound find? If I were you, John, I should submit my case to the Rockefeller or the Guggenheim people, and with, I am sure, the willing co-operation of the Canadian Government, have that field excavated by trained archaeologists. Harvard has them by the dozens. So has Yale."

After supper they all sat round the driftwood fire and popped corn. Mrs. Desmond, who had a really good contralto voice, sang several parts of Grieg's *Holberg Suite*. Professor Desmond did his college imitation of Maurice Chevalier. Summoning up his memories of the folk tale collections of Asbjörnson and Moe, Dr. Krehan told a story about a lad who had an eating match with a troll. Not to be outdone, Professor Desmond then capped the Norse tale with a comparable Paul Bunyan adventure straight out of the Minnesota lumber camps. The clock hands had sped on to ten before Mrs. Desmond noticed that the girls' bedtime was long since overdue.

"My!" she said. "And tomorrow a school day, too!"

The men lingered a while over their nightcap. But it wasn't more than a half hour later that Karen heard her father call out good night to his guest; then switch off the light at the staircase. She waited till she was sure Dr. Krehan had settled down in his room, which was just next to hers, on the second floor landing. Then, slipping a plastic-covered flashlight from her dresser drawer, she crept downstairs to test the bolts. The porch door bolt was in place. So was the catch of the back screen. The moon had just risen over the poplar trees, and the Council Rock glistened cold and lonely in the silver radiance. For the first time in two whole days she felt reasonably secure. On her way through the dining room again she touched the sword hilt for good luck, as one sometimes touches wood.

"Patience, cousin Thorbjorn," she said softly. "It will not be long now."

Just then a shifting log chinked in the grate. Or was it that the sword blade sang low in answer? Or in warning, like Excalibur and Durendal in *My Bookhouse* back on the nursery shelves in the city house? For her vigil was far from over yet.

Dr. Krehan could not get to sleep. Karen's eyes began to burn in smarting weariness as she lay in bed and listened to him pace round and round his room. She wondered if her father heard and was awake in the room below. Perhaps not. Moira and Sheila certainly slept soundly enough in their room across the hall. Once he went into the bathroom and poured himself a drink of water. Heart pounding, Karen waited, one hand on her door knob, in case he decided to go downstairs. Back went the restless footsteps. Back to bed she crept. She must have dozed a little after that, for the next thing she heard was the porch door bolt being shot. In dry-mouthed panic she opened her door. The door next to hers was ajar. She peeped in. Dr. Krehan was not in his bed.

Then it was that Karen made the snap decision on which so much was to depend. She woke Sheila and Moira to serve as her strategic reserve, in case her own counter thrust failed. Her only other alternative was to waken Father. But, on the whole, she thought afterward that she had done the right thing. If nothing had happened, it would have been a pity to frighten Mother who had begun to look a little wan these latter months. Whatever happened, she knew that the younger sisters would follow her orders. Father very well might not have. He knew nothing of what was up. There was no time any more to put him in possession of the necessary facts. If she had made a mistake at all, it lay in her not having told him everything while there was still time to talk. But there had never been the necessary opportunity — or, if that was being not quite frank about the matter, something had always drawn her back from the brink of revelation.

In yawning, desperate haste the children slipped on tennis shoes and bathrobes. Quietly they went down the stairs and out onto the moon-drenched verandah. As luck would have it, Dr. Krehan was still standing by the wall. Even as they came out, however, without noticing them he wheeled about and marched up the beach away from the Scotts' great poplar and toward the right tip of the sandy crescent as one faced the lake. The moon shone full overhead so that the white sand and still cold lake were bright as at midday. There was a little covert in the velvet shadow of the retaining walls. Taking advantage of these uniform patches of darkness, the three girls stalked their guest. Some four hundred yards down the shore it happened. The seal man stepped out into the moon glimmer from behind an uprooted poplar. He carried a snub-nosed revolver in his right hand.

"*Guten Abend, Herr Doktor Krehan*," he said silkily. "We met last in Teheran, in August of 1940, I believe. A long time ago, *nicht wahr?*"

Dr. Krehan's breath hissed in sharply.

"Gromov!" he said.

The seal man bowed.

"At your service, as usual, *Herr Doktor*," he said mockingly.

Karen turned to her questioning sisters, finger on lips in the immemorial and automatic gesture for silence. Quickly and silently they drew back several paces to where, in an agony of concentration, she gave them their directions; and never in her life was the slender red-haired kinswoman of Sigrid of Laagen and of American pioneers to show higher capacity for tactical improvisation. The respective missions she entrusted to Sheila and Moira were exactly suited to their different temperaments.

The dreamy Moira was to go straight to the Council Rock, and there call aloud for Great Bear and the Viking. They would both be sure to come to her call — she would see Great Bear, even if she could not see the Viking. Then she should tell them where to find Karen and Dr. Krehan, who was the man of whom the knucklebones spoke, the elder one who stayed in her father's lodge.

Where he would be, Karen would be. For, if it was at all possible, she was determined to stay on the seal man's track.

As for Sheila, among whose variegated accomplishments had always been an uncanny accuracy in remembering and dialing telephone numbers, she should crawl into Dr. Thibault's already half-shuttered up house, by the secret way all the beach children knew of and Dr. Thibault didn't, and use his phone to call a certain number and ask for Mr. Christopher Conboy of the Federal Bureau of Investigation. It would be light enough to see, so bright was the full moon, even if the electric switch was cut off. The little window by the telephone alcove was never shuttered. The telephone stayed in all winter in case it was necessary to locate the doctor, who often dropped in to his beach home, at all seasons, with some medical crony or other.

Karen made Sheila repeat the number three times. Mohawk 7800. If Mr. Conboy could not be found, she was to tell the night operator three things. First, Dr. Gottfried Krehan of West Berlin was being kidnaped from Crescent Beach, Ontario. Second, no later than yesterday a foreign aviator had buried a parachute with printing on it in a queer alphabet — very likely Russian — near to where Dr. Krehan had been captured. Third, they must hurry. Hurry. Hurry. Hurry.

As the earnest little ghosts in bathrobes crept quietly away, Karen looked at the luminous dial of her wrist watch. It read 1:15. Then she stole, as close as she dared, to where the seal man was still talking to Dr. Krehan.

The seal man put his hand in his jacket pocket to draw out what Karen supposed would be another cigarette. It was a whistle, instead. A soundless one, apparently, for, though he blew on it several times, she heard nothing. He replaced the shining tube in his pocket.

"Very ingenious, your scientists," he said, grinning. "This is one of their latest high frequency developments — for men, not dogs. For men, that is, who are equipped with the proper pocket-size receiving sets. Like the faithful Vladimir who will soon be here — and Kostya, too. You will remember Vladimir and Kostya, I believe. If not, you will recognize them. The years have made remarkably little change in their appearances."

"Yes," said Dr. Krehan, stiff-lipped. "I remember Vladimir and Kostya. But I want to remind you that the one-time Nazi scientists of whom you speak are not now and never were 'my scientists,' as you choose to call them."

The seal man blew out his lips judiciously.

"To give the devil his due, Herr Doktor," he said agreeably, "one should admit you were never on the side of the Nazi-Fascists. Although, I should remind you in my turn, there was good ideological precedent for such a temporary *mariage de convenance.* Take our case, for example. There was the liaison of August, 1939, and the divorce of July, 1941. Since 1945 there has been another morganatic marriage between us and certain scientists and military men from the Reich. But you will hardly deny, my friend, that since your — shall we say, rude? — departure from our hospitable custody, you have been serving the pluto-democracies, and now the Adenauer Reich, both in your old capacity as physicist extraordinary and now, in quite a new capacity, as political scientist nonpareil."

"I do not deny it," said Dr. Krehan more stiffly than before. "I owe a great debt of honor to the country which took me in when I was homeless. And another debt of love to the shattered country of my fathers. But let me warn you, Smerdyakov — "

"Gromov is the name," the seal man said with an ugly smile. "And do not think I do not see the insult. We, too, read Dostoevsky."

"I am sorry for the mistake, Gromov," said Dr. Krehan ironically. "But in my terms it was a natural one. You see, I do not think of you new men as either cultural Neanderthalers or as men without umbilical cords. Those are Western images — good ones, but still Western. No, to me your kind are all Smerdyakovs — criminal and illegitimate degenerates who have taken over the human house of Karamazov. But to resume. Let me warn you, Gromov. I have shown myself a great fool to fall thus into your trap. Nevertheless — "

It was the seal man's turn to be ironical.

"Not so great a fool, perhaps," he interrupted. "I think you are underrating both our subtlety and our assiduity. Take our assiduity first. Quite obviously you have not detected it, but you have been under constant surveillance by an American Communist operative ever since you first took up residence in the *Cosmos Club.*"

"One minute!" said Dr. Krehan, thunderstruck. "I have indeed been a fool! Your American operative — is he small and dark like a Vizier from *The Arabian Nights?*"

"I do not know about *The Arabian Nights*," said Gromov. "But yes. He was small and dark. Levantine, I suppose. And *was*, not *is*, my dear *Herr Doktor*. *Was* is the proper tense here."

"I do not understand," said Dr. Krehan.

"I mean," said Gromov, boasting, "he had to be discarded. Very near here, as a matter of fact. Out by that pier. I have his one remaining chattel here in my pocket. You see, he had been careless."

Gromov took out the page he had torn from the tabloid and waved it languidly, before putting it back in his pocket.

"But," he said. "As you say — to resume. Take our subtlety next. We owe our present successful gambit to the old *Gestapo* dossier on yourself which records that, at the full of the moon, *Herr Doktor* Gottfried Krehan, licentiate of Weimar, Bonn, and Heidelberg, grows restless, smokes excessively, likes to take long walks at night, unattended. It was really risking nothing on our part. If we lost this trick — as, of course, we have not — there would have been other chances. Then our assiduity could have been brought into play again. As you remember, we are both patient and ingenious."

"Yes," said Dr. Krehan, "you are both patient and ingenious. Like all savages. But you will please permit me to complete what I started to say. I am not quite so great a fool as you take me for. A letter is in the post now — a belated precaution, I admit, and a feeble one, but still a precaution. I wrote it in Washington and mailed it this afternoon in Buffalo. It is addressed to my host, Professor Desmond, at his Buffalo residence, and it acquaints him with my own theory as to the reason for any mysterious disappearance his guest might be involved in. Needless to say, Gromov, your name figures prominently in my conjectural reconstruction."

The seal man scrutinized his nails in a languid manner.

"I thank you for the compliment, *Herr Professor*," he said. "But — a rather primitive expedient, don't you think? A letter is — a letter. While, as for us, a seaplane is — a seaplane."

Gromov made a dramatic gesture in the direction of the sheltered moonlit cove at the right end of the crescent, at the other end of the long curve from the old pier. With engines banked, a giant trimotored plane glided to a perfect landing on its huge pontoons, and lay to silently off shore, rocking gently in the land swell. A white bear was painted on its fuselage. Over the insigne stood the same sort of queer lettering Karen had noticed on the parachute strip.

"May I introduce you to your flagship, *Herr Doktor?*" said Gromov. "*The White Bear*. Personally, I should have preferred calling it *Sea Gull* in honor of Chekhov. Or *Albatross* for Lermontov. But *White Bear* is not so bad, either. We improve in every way, you see. Aesthetically. Scientifically. Even geography aids. It is not so very far to Siberia over the Pole as the *Bear* flies. You were saying something about a letter?"

Dr. Krehan bowed like an automaton.

"You have the *force majeure*, Gromov," he said. "I do not question that. But a letter flies fast, too. After its reception, there is always such a thing as a diplomatic protest."

"Ah, diplomacy," said the seal man, pursing his lips again. "How long that *bourgeois* concept is in yielding to the people's *Diktat!* Still, as you say, it is a factor. It is true we are as impervious to *démarches* as any state in history. We can be bland. We can deny . . . *Herr Doktor* Krehan? Was there not a Nobel physicist and political scientist of the name? Missing? How regrettable! A letter accusing us? How unfortunate! The poor man must have suffered from a persecution mania. The result, undoubtedly, of overwork on the new West German election laws. You see, it can be done, if, of course, the protesters cannot produce a *corpus delicti*. Even so. You have a point. The many diplomatic protests mount up. If there were a way — "

Karen had underestimated the seal man. Like a great cat he wheeled and lunged into the shadow of the protecting wall. Before she could scream, a hand was clapped across her mouth.

"There is a way, after all," said the seal man, motioning to Dr. Krehan with his revolver. "Come here, *Herr Doktor*. I believe the American child is a friend of yours. A pity wrist watches have to glint in the moonlight, is it not? But *mon cher professeur, revenons à nos moutons*, as the French comrades say. In other words, let us get back to business. We, too, can write letters to American professors. American professors should be old enough by now to learn the political facts of life. That, for instance, there are such things as daughters and such things as hostages. That hostages can be treated well or ill depending on the behavior of those at whose expense they are held. That if — on our suggestion, of course, though they will hardly recognize that — the American Government chooses to conclude that the disappearance of Dr. Krehan is another Burgess-Maclean affair, Professor Desmond will do well to keep silent. You should realize all this as well as anyone else, *Herr Doktor*. Especially on a night of full moon like this one."

There were blank spaces in the life of Gottfried Krehan of which he never spoke to anyone. Karen remembered having heard her father say some such thing to Mother. Now he began to sob there in the moonlight. Sob horribly. It shook her. She had never heard a man cry before.

"For the love of God, Gromov!" said Dr. Krehan. "Let the child go! I will come with you without protest."

"With or without protest," said the seal man, blowing again on his soundless whistle, "you will come with us in any case. So will the child."

Gromov laughed an ugly laugh and began to speak in a monotone as if reciting from a record.

" 'Displays marked restlessness and incipient emotional instability on nights of full moon, possibly because he associates full moon with night seizure of daughter by first marriage, Elsa Krehan, aged ten years. Daughter died while in protective custody of *Geheimnis-staatspolizei*, Weimar Branch.' Did not Marx say all history was cyclical, *Herr Doktor*? Even in such trivial details as little girls, secret police, and the employment of remedial violence?"

A rubber boat had put off from the great plane. As it drew near shore, the seal man took his right hand from the mouth of the terrified girl and shifted the revolver into it from his left.

"So," he said gently, almost caressingly, and quite absently, striking her heavily over the temple with the gun butt. Karen had one glimpse of Dr. Krehan's white piteous face swelling before her like a carnival balloon, only immeasurably more gigantic. Then darkness engulfed her.

When the child came to her senses again, she was lying in the bottom of the rubber boat, a dull pain throbbing in her head. The small craft rocked in the ground swell. Little wavelets lapped and sucked all around her. The great seaplane was moored immediately alongside. It, too, lifted and sank on the strengthening current. She saw, once or twice, lightning flashes on the horizon, miles away over the steel plants which marked the southern approach to Buffalo. There was a storm blowing up.

A rope ladder led from the rubber boat up into the aircraft's cabin entrance. Dr. Krehan, Karen decided, must be already inside. The seal man and the two crewmen, whom he had called Vladimir and Kostya, were standing in the cabin door, talking in their own tongue. She had an impression, nevertheless, that they were speaking of her, and that the argument was growing heated. But there was no time to listen. For another sort of conversation altogether, and one that she could understand, was also going on within earshot.

Moira had done her work well. The Viking and the Indian were standing on the edge of the shore where sand and water met. Though the rubber boat must have been better than two hundred yards distant, Karen was able to hear their voices and see their faces perfectly. Possibly it was the blow on her head — she did not think so, however, neither then nor afterward — but tonight, some-how, the Viking and the Indian seemed different. Huger. More symbolic. As if sitting in judgment. Their faces were grave and measured like those of giant judges. As she watched, the mighty figures appeared to grow before her until their heads towered into the very stars. Two years later, when Karen went to college and learned to love the Roman poets, she read of the tutelary spirits who haunted rock and stream and woodland, and remembered this thing that once, long before, had come to her on the marches of girlhood. If ever there were genii loci, Thorbjorn and Great Bear were they.

"You saw the blow," said Thorbjorn, raising a mailed fist to the autumn stars. "Our ancient peace has been profaned."

"It was a white man who struck the blow," said Great Bear sternly, "and a white child who suffered it. It is ever the way of the pale usurper. It was thus they smote down our red brothers, giving no quarter, stealing from us our rivers and lakes and forests. What have they done with the fair land they stole? The rivers are fouled. The black earth bleeds red into the sea. The green grass dies beneath their blocks of stone. Their evil smoke hides the sun and moon. Shall we come between the white savages when they quarrel?"

"I was of the white folk once," said Thorbjorn. "I remember that. I cannot forget it, though it was many moons ago. The child is my kinswoman, and the kinswoman of Sigrid of Laagen. Also, I do not like this smiting of children. We did not use to do so in Sognefjord. Her father is a fool, but not unkindly. Her mother, my kinswoman also, is with child, and so is sacred to the guarding presences. Besides, these men are Scythian scum. I knew them of old when we rowed through the *Rus* on our way to Micklegarth to join the Emperor's Varangians. They could never stand against us, for all their numbers which were as the sands of the sea. Again, I do not like their using our brother the Bear on this flying ship of theirs. As for your people, has it not come to your ears, my brother, that they have fought for the men of this land in two great wars? Are not the New World men your brothers now, though they were not so in the beginning?"

The great bronze profile softened somewhat.

"It is true," said the Indian. "They have undone some of the ancient wrong. My people flourish again in the northern fields and on the western tablelands. Red men live in amity with men of white and black and yellow skin alike. They serve the Great Spirit as they will. And no one says them nay. I have heard that in the lands from which these others come the Great Spirit must hide His face. It is true, my brother. It is even as you say. The peoples of this land we know and love have not done perfectly. But they have done well. Moreover, I, too, can remember the days of my tribe. The sister of this little one is *orenda*, and wears the moonstone and arrowhead of my people."

"Then," said the Viking, his voice rising, "we shall hunt the Bear once again. We who thought our hunting days were over!"

Karen saw him raise his spear, and the Indian flex his crooked bow, both crying aloud as they did so. Her blood chilled when the Iroquois ululations rang over the water. Thorbjorn's shouting was hoarser, but no less terrifying. She could make out only that it ended:

"Thor! Thor! Thor!"

The seal man and his friends heard it, too. They crowded to the gangway. Karen could see Dr. Krehan's white face behind them. Then there came a metallic twang and the lance stuck, quivering, in the side of the flying ship, only an inch or so from the seal man's head. A bow string was plucked; and an arrow flew to its mark beside the spear. In a panic Vladimir and Kostya fired their carbines over her head. The volleyed shot bounded back, in staccato riccochet of echoed sound, off the flanks of the crescent.

Then she heard the Viking laughter as the mailed warrior began splashing out to the plane. Great Bear's bow string sounded twice again. Two more arrows flashed to join the first one. Vladimir and Kostya fired over and over till their automatic rifles jammed. Cursing, the seal man brandished his revolver at his two subordinates. He appeared to be trying to herd them back into the pilot's nacelle and, perhaps, would have succeeded, if the blond-bearded warrior had not clambered up the rope ladder, and, shaking the seal man like some small animal, dropped him contemptuously into the rubber boat where he lay without moving. Thorbjorn looked Karen straight in the eyes.

"You owe me a sword for this night's good work, little red kinswoman," he said, still laughing, for the battle mirth had not yet left him. "And not just any sword. One smithied by Asgrim of Lillehammer, greatest armorer in the Northland. Then we will be quits. And more than quits, too."

Vladimir and Kostya still cowered in the cabin entrance. But there must have been another of the invaders, one with instructions to stay hidden in the pilot's nacelle. For, with a thunderous roar, the engines started revving up. At that moment, a searchlight was trained on the white plane from the beach, and, from the lake, a Coast Guard cutter fired a warning shot across her propellers. The two boarding parties arrived simultaneously in motorboats while the plane motors spluttered to a coughing stop. The Canadians had the advantage of being closer to the scene of action; but radio worked swiftly, too. The cutter had had only two miles to come. Gromov and company offered no further resistance. They understood the principle of *force majeure* too well for that.

Sheila had more than done her work well. She had exceeded instructions with the most glorious results; and next morning Karen ritually acknowledged her valor by conferring on her the prized plastic Royal Mountie she had bought with her own hoarded pocket money one picnic day in the Commissary Room of Old Fort Erie. As things had turned out, it was a most appropriate decoration.

Sheila's exploit all seemed so simple when one reconstructed it. At the time, though, it had called for the most unflagging resolution and quick thinking, standing there in the fitful moonlight that shone in through the Thibaults' curtains, and this after the scary entry by crawling through the secret sand passageway under the house, too. But dialing had always been one of Sheila's attainments; and, besides, she still had in her pocket the program for the Military Tattoo of Saturday afternoon, with the telephone number of the Mounties' cantonment on it under a picture of a stalwart Mountie on horseback. So, after getting through to Mr. Christopher Conboy of the American F.B.I., Sheila had coolly rung up a very sleepy Sergeant of the Royal Mounted Police. Under the circumstances, she could be forgiven her vast disappointment at their not arriving in the celebrated crimson parade uniform. To make up for this deficiency they carried guns a-plenty and, before that long night was finally over, Lieutenant Alexander MacPherson had won the child's heart by giving her a warm Scots kiss. It was a triumph for earth over fire and water. If Karen had been the only one to see the Viking, and if Great Bear had claimed Moira for his Lodge, Sheila could always point out that she had been the sole legatee of a Mountie's kiss.

To his vast relief, Mr. Christopher Conboy found it unnecessary to explain the presence of a United States Coast Guard Cutter in Canadian territorial waters. He did observe international etiquette, however, by making sure it was the Canadian officer who took the men into custody. Extradition, as Lieutenant MacPherson remarked to him with a saturnine grimace, would prove an easy process, if necessary. During the questioning, which took place on the beach, Dr. Krehan served as interpreter for Vladimir and Kostya and, on more than one occasion, for a very shaken Gromov. The fourth man, the one in the nacelle, refused to speak at all. Throughout the oral process, Dr. Krehan stroked Karen's head — her aching temples had begun to feel very light again — and smiled at the wide eyes of the two smaller sisters.

"Very obliging of the beggars to panic so conveniently," said Lieutenant MacPherson, who had been in the R.A.F., to Agent Conboy. "If it hadn't been for the infernal din of all that firing, we might have been minutes longer locating them. In fact, it is entirely possible they could have gotten away. I wonder what frightened them. What in the world did they think they were firing at?"

"They were firing at the Viking and the Indian," said Karen, feeling like Alice in Looking Glass Land, what with the strange faces ringing her in the searchlight glare, and with the growing giddiness in her head. "But bullets can't hurt Thorbjorn or Great Bear."

"The Viking!" said Lieutenant MacPherson. "And the Indian! Do you suppose the child is getting delirious?"

"No," said Dr. Krehan quietly, "I do not think she is delirious. Remember what our good friend, Gromov, said in his deposition."

Lieutenant MacPherson consulted his notes.

"Gromov?" he said.

"The leader," said Dr. Krehan. "The one who speaks English when he chooses."

"Oh, yes," said Lieutenant MacPherson. "I see he goes on at length about a golden-bearded man in armor and a tall Indian with a bow. I put it all down to too much vodka."

"I can assure you, Lieutenant," said Dr. Krehan just as quietly, "Comrade Gromov never touches liquor on a mission."

Then Dr. Krehan smiled a grim smile. For a moment, thought Karen, he looked just like the Viking.

"He has a more dangerous weakness, as it happens," he said. "He likes to boast. It means you will be able to hang him without much trouble. You do hang in this country, do you not? The *corpus delicti* is out near that old pier over to your left. I suggest that you preserve the newspaper page found in his pocket with the utmost care. It probably has the victim's finger prints on it."

"Thank you," said Lieutenant MacPherson, startled, but duly noting down what he had been told.

Mr. Conboy had a searchlight directed on the seaplane. From the shore, another finger of radiance played up and down the white ship like a finger exercise for white keys only. Then it shut off.

"I noticed," Mr. Conboy said in explanation, "that Vladimir's and Kostya's statements have a great deal to say about spears and arrows. Not much like the atomic warfare they're preparing for, is it? Well, according to their story, that fuselage out there should now be bristling like a porcupine with stone age missiles. But there are no spears or arrows in it now. Not one."

"No," said Dr. Krehan, "you are right. There are none there now."

Mr. Conboy looked quizzically at the German.

"You imply," he said, "that perhaps there were some there a little while ago? Did you see a Viking, Dr. Krehan?"

Dr. Krehan shrugged in a very un-American gesture.

"I saw something, Mr. Conboy," he said evenly. "I heard something, too. As an old and weary pragmatist who has tried to be, in his day, an honest agnostic, I commit myself no further. You can, if you wish, repose on the hypothesis of collective hallucination involving three American children, one political scientist of more ambiguous extraction, and four men of the New Order that has expressly repudiated the traditional supernatural. The whole induced by nonexistent vodka."

Dr. Krehan laughed to himself.

"I will admit," he continued, "that our present incident does not precisely belong to the realm of the 'traditional supernatural.' What realm does it belong to? What was it, you ask? I confess I do not know. For myself, I invoke the famous line of your English poet: *There are more things in heaven and earth, Horatio. . . .* But surely you know the quotation better than I."

Mr. Conboy was not quite sure he did. In any event, he thought some things were just as well not noted down. He found the coming on of rain and the simultaneous arrival of an anxious Professor and Mrs. Desmond a welcome pair of diversions. In addition to the sleeping Kristin, a practical Mrs. Desmond had caught up several umbrellas, and this despite the excitement of having discovered three empty beds in the girls' rooms. She had assumed, of course, that the children had been allured to the searchlight clamor at the far right end of the beach on the same principle as moth and candle or little boy and fire siren.

Mr. Conboy, whom Professor Desmond hailed familiarly as "Chris," was mercifully circumspect in disabusing her. A family man himself, he noticed her condition at once. He also knew shock when he saw it; and he did not like the wan look on Karen's face. So he suggested to Professor Desmond that the older girl be given a strong cup of tea forthwith, and that he should see to it that the tea was laced with a tablespoon of brandy. Out over the lake the thunder began to mutter in a desultory fashion.

The crowning glory of the adventure still awaited Karen. She was propped up on pillows in the double brass bedstead in Father's and Mother's downstairs bedroom where she had not slept since her crib days of twelve years before. Sleepily she sank down in the warm coverlets, yawning luxuriously, the events of the past fifty-six hours coursing, phantasmagoria-like, through her relaxed mind. Rain drops began to drum on the shingled roof. Her bed felt like a ship. The waves had a muffled roar about them down on the beach. The window curtain flapped as the night wind freshened. As so often happened to her just before sleeping, Karen began to think of the bronze Oseberg ship on the mantel at home. Once more the craft made its gray dawn landfall off Martha's Vineyard. Waves broke in intervals of spray around the dragon figurehead. She yawned again, and snuggled into the bed clothes. The pictures kept on before her eyes. Helmeted men were landing in the booming Massachusetts surf. But no! That could not be. Her dream was wrong. The Oseberg was a Queen's barge, Thorbjorn had said — Thorbjorn! She sat bolt upright against the pillows, eyes feverish bright in a flushed little face.

"Father," she said in a clear voice, "I must take Thorbjorn the sword."

Mrs. Desmond was just putting out a restraining hand, when Dr. Krehan stopped her. He said something in a low voice. When he had finished, Mrs. Desmond nodded. There were troubles of the mind and heart more terrible than possible concussion. All she said was:

"Put on your bathrobe, darling."

It was no longer a night of stars and moon when Karen, looking very slender in her plaid bathrobe and the reindeer slippers cousin Olaf had sent last Christmas from Trondhjem, set foot on the planked walk in the rear of the house. The trees were still there, however, lashing their black plumes in the rising dawn wind like knights in tournament or Indians locked in death grapple. When the lightning flashed, as it did now at closer and closer intervals, the resemblance to wrestling warriors increased.

Thorbjorn was waiting by the Council Rock, Great Bear and White Owl beside him. The Indians said nothing, only smiled, as the child presented the sword, which she held by the smiting blade, cross hilt foremost, to the Viking warrior. He kissed the blade, let it rest lightly for an instant on her red curls, touched her on the cheek once, whispered:

"Thank you, little kinswoman!"

And was gone.

Then the storm broke in earnest. The rain poured down in equinoctial fury. Thunderclaps shook the chimney. The lake surged up to the retaining wall. As Karen, rubbed warm again and clothed in fresh pajamas, entered the caverns of grateful sleep at last, she heard her father say to Dr. Krehan:

"A Wagnerian finale, eh, Gottfried? It was right to humor her, I suppose. Let the sword lie there till morning."

And Dr. Krehan replied:

"I should call it rather a Sibelius finale. The saga essence is too pure for Wagner. And, my friend, I should not bet on our recovering the sword in the morning."

It was not for some years that Karen was to realize that, for once, her father had been wrong. On the other hand, scientist though he was, Dr. Krehan had been right. It was pure Sibelius. Or, perhaps, it would be truer to say that he had been half right. Something had gone on that could not be expressed in musical or literary analogues. The marches of myth were fading again. The gods and heroes were gone. So was childhood — and girlhood, too. Like a Valkyrie she had that night ridden into womanhood, there to possess her fair estate.

Dr. Krehan was pouring himself another finger of whiskey, when

Professor Desmond called to him, in a low voice, from the bottom of the staircase.

"Come here, Gottfried," he said. "I want you to take a look at the kid."

Karen was sleeping soundly now, her red hair soft aureoled against the white pillow. Observing her as she slept, Dr. Krehan noted that she looked more like a woman than a child, even though, at the moment Gromov struck her down, she had looked the veriest child.

"What do you think?" asked Professor Desmond anxiously.

Dr. Krehan sighed to himself a little, as his fingers probed her head. What did he think? That there were many things that did not bear much thinking on. That little Elsa, had she lived, would, at some point, have looked like this sleeping child. That the sensitive European, like himself, always felt the presence of *genii loci* on the elder continent, even as the old Chinese made due allowance, in their ancient land, for *Feng-shui*, those same elemental spirits of earth and air. But he had never expected to find the spirits of place so strong in this new America which, after all, was not so very new, either.

He thought also that the great myths were profoundly true in their recalling the primordial closeness of heaven and earth. He had read somewhere that the bird and animal cries of the shamans were intended to restore the mystic rapport between man and beast which was in the beginning, when Adam named and Eve talked with the animals, and when, as a great Doctor of this little sleeping girl's Church once said, "in the state of innocence, man by his command ruled over the other animals." When, also, History was not yet, and Time still touched Timelessness. As, perhaps, for the fortunate ones it still did.

Well, children were touched with that old kind of magic, some more than others. Already, though, it must be passing even from this favored child. No matter. Another even stronger, realer magic would one day come to her, if she were lucky. The magic of love.

That was what Dr. Krehan thought. What he said was merely:

"I shouldn't worry, if I were you, John. Youth is resilient, you know. No school for a week. Keep her in bed, and quiet. A doctor in the morning. That is all that is indicated. No harm has been done."

Dr. Krehan had been right about Sibelius and Professor Desmond wrong. On one point, though, Professor Desmond had been right and Dr. Krehan wrong, even if, as so often happened in life, Professor Desmond had been right for the wrong reason, and Dr. Krehan wrong for the right reason. The sword was there in the morning. What was more, the Viking was there, too. The torrential rain — six inches had fallen in eight hours, Buffalo streets and cellars had been flooded — had caused a minor landslide at the foot of the Council Rock. A clean sandy burial cavern had been exposed. In it lay a helmeted skeleton, holding, in one bony hand, the sword from Gorham's field. Two slighter skeletons — one that of a tall man, the other that of a slim woman — slept beside him. Kristin had found them first. She had wakened early to install a television set in her Indian fort, and had then strayed out into the drenched back yard. Her announcement, while the others sat at breakfast, was characteristically direct.

"There are," she stated, "some Halloween bones in the back yard, and they've got our sword."

The stampede out the back screen door was general, except for Karen who was sipping her orange juice, back against her downstairs pillow throne.

"By George!" said Professor Desmond, viewing the relics. There were Indian artifacts alongside the slighter skeletons. "That tears it! Uncanny how the sword slipped down into his hand."

"Do you really think it slipped down into his hand, John?" asked Dr. Krehan. "But no matter. You've got your Viking all right, and two Indians as well, it seems. Now you don't need Harvard or Yale."

"No," said Professor Desmond thoughtfully. "Not Harvard or Yale. But we still need the University of Toronto and the Canadian Government. This is a big show now."

"First," said Dr. Krehan, "we should tell the child."

"Yes," said Professor Desmond uncertainly. "We must break it to Karen. She's even got a name for the old chap, you know. Called him Thorbjorn last night."

"Yes, John. I know," said Dr. Krehan.

"Will it upset her, do you think?" asked Professor Desmond.

"I do not think it will upset her," said Dr. Krehan.

It didn't. Not one little bit. When Professor Desmond had finished his account, Karen only sighed. But it was a peaceful, almost a happy sigh.

"I should like to see him now," was all she said.

Professor Desmond looked mutely at Dr. Krehan. The older man inclined his head.

"All right, then," said Professor Desmond gently, steadying her on his arm.

As the slender child stood looking down into the pit, Mrs. Desmond turned aside, tears in her eyes. Without saying a word, Dr. Krehan patted her hand.

"Come now," he said to Karen after a minute or so. "Time to go back to bed again."

When she was once more ensconced against the pillows, Professor Desmond reopened the subject.

"Now," he said, jollying her, "get ready for the news reels. Conboy and MacPherson have managed to hold off the reporters today. When the reporters get hold of this new development, you'll be on every movie screen in the country. And every television screen, too."

"Oh," said Karen unhappily. "Will Thorbjorn, too?"

"Of course he will," said Professor Desmond enthusiastically. "Sutton Hoo is nowhere beside this. This is the biggest find since Tutankh-a-men."

"I don't think he will like that," said Karen. "You see, he was such a handsome Viking, and now he is only bones. And what will happen to him after that?"

"Why," said Professor Desmond, "I suppose they'll put him in a Museum. If they do, our names will be on the case as well. You see he really belongs to the Canadian Government."

"No, I don't see," said Karen angrily. "I don't want my name on an old glass case. It isn't decent. How would you like your grave exposed to view? And Thorbjorn doesn't belong to any government. He belongs to himself because he belonged to God."

"You know, John," said Dr. Krehan, "there is something in what the child says. I have seen the bones in Dachau and Sachsenhausen. And I have seen at first hand what happened to the Government that thought it owned those bones and the men who once belonged to them. Our friend out there goes back a long, long way. But does that make any difference essentially? So does the human condition go back a long, long way."

Professor Desmond almost snorted.

"I didn't know you were a religious man, Gottfried," he said in what, for him, was almost a contemptuous tone.

"I don't suppose I am," said Dr. Krehan. "I never have been. Still . . ."

He was silent.

"Still?" said Professor Desmond irritably. "What do you mean — 'still'?"

"Nothing," said Dr. Krehan.

Then Karen returned to the attack.

"If Mr. Gromov's government," she asked, "were to get hold of Thorbjorn, what would they do with him?"

"Why," said Professor Desmond, "put him in a Museum, of course. As any intelligent government would do. . . ."

He stopped shamefaced.

"Exactly," said Dr. Krehan. "As any intelligent government would do."

Dr. Krehan began to laugh.

"The dialectic of humane instinct," he said. "Of immemorial human tradition, of Christianity, in fact, and any other religion you care to mention, against the inhuman dialectic of the passionless, emasculated, statistical reason. The child has you in a cleft stick, John. I think you have two Philadelphia lawyers in the family."

"I think Karen is right, dear," said Mrs. Desmond shyly. "After all, it isn't as if he were an utter stranger, either. Actually, he's probably one of my cousins."

"Nine hundred years back, maybe," said Professor Desmond sourly. "A woman's reason."

"A human reason, John," said Dr. Krehan. "A Pascalian reason. *La coeur a ses raisons que la raison ne connaît point — The heart has reasons that reason cannot comprehend.*"

Professor Desmond did not argue further; and that afternoon when, with Karen looking on, Dr. Krehan and the two older girls, plus Kristin and Bozo Belinda, began filling in the cavern again, he pitched in willingly enough.

There was some debate over the question of a burial service.

"He must have been a Christian," said Mrs. Desmond. "His sword had a cross hilt."

"He didn't talk much like a Christian," said Karen doubtfully. "And he was always calling on Thor."

"Oh, he was a Christian all right," said Dr. Krehan. "Everyone was a Christian in Europe then. There is even *Ave Maria* scratched on the Kensington rune-stone. I don't suppose he worked very hard at it, of course. But do Christians today?"

In the end the family compromised by scratching a rude cross on the white boulder over the burial pit and having Moira quaver Schubert's *Ave Maria* over it. Sheila brought some autumn wild flowers from Gorham's field, where the sword was found, and Mrs. Desmond worked them into four tiny wreaths. Professor Desmond stood uncomfortably about during the service. Dr. Krehan thought on some lines of the great Augustine which he had always loved. Lines about man's "unquiet heart."

They went to bed early that night, and slept the sleep of the exhausted just. All but John Desmond. He lay awake, staring bleakly into the darkness, thinking on the chance he had blown because he could not stand against his wife and daughters and the German friend who had so unaccountably backed their sentimentalism. The greatest archaeological find since Heinrich Schliemann dug up Troy! And where was it now? Buried — not excavated, buried! — in his own back yard!

But, if there was a Sancho Panza craving wealth and notoriety in the soul of every man, in the soul of all professors worth their salt Sancho's master, Don Quixote, reigned supreme. So, after an interval, it proved with John Desmond. By the time his watch registered three a.m., the Knight of La Mancha had resumed his usual sway; and all was well again under the weathered shingles of the little beach house.

CHAPTER ELEVEN

Farewell to Summer

MR. GROMOV was sure to hang under Canadian law. But, while the flood of newsmen into the quiet lives of the Desmonds was formidable enough, it was not nearly so formidable as it would have been, had it suited the book of any one of the three governments involved to make much of the case. To the Soviets, Comrade Gromov was expendable. He had blundered; and he could pay the penalty. To the Western allies it was more convenient not to seem to be interfering in West German electoral concerns. So the nine days' wonder of the press centered on the murder of Mr. Tikjan. Not on the diplomatic incident. Not at all on the heroes who once again slept their sleep, undisturbed there in the sweet northern earth.

Summer still clung sweetly in pockets and crannies of October. In the rose beds especially. There was a post card from Berlin, saying that all was well with Dr. Krehan. There were letters from Jack indicating that he would definitely be home by the end of the first week in November. Mrs. Desmond put down her son's latest letter and her glasses together, and thought ahead to a fortnight after that when her woman's time should have come upon her once again. Other than this, the outer world receded in the trance of autumn weather.

By Halloween life in the Desmond house on Hurst Monceux had resumed its even, mellow, between-the-rubrics flavor. Professor Desmond raked leaves, stacking them in bronze, undulating swales that seemed to breathe, as if alive, whenever a breath of wind stirred over them. A few torpid flies blundered by, intent on a squashed pear on the lawn, the usual precision of their buzzing intentions numbed by the time of year. Two cawing grackles quarreled over some red spears of crab grass. Rajah and Ranee, whose Durbar pelts perfectly suited this season of the leaves' crimson suttee, basked on the terrace, too indolent to do anything at all about the wrangling birds. So did old Sillerton Jackson whose inky black just as perfectly suited Halloween.

The lawn was still an intense green on this last day of October. So was the Desmonds' single apple tree against which the ripe apples stood out in blood-red relief, but a laughing, scarlet-lipped blood-red, as if some gay dryad had kissed them crimson in pure joy. Autumn was an apple, a keeping fruit. Autumn was better even than spring. A spring orchard was a flagon of perfume. An autumn orchard was a tankard of Canary. The apple began as a maiden and ended as a cider-drinking Mistress Quickly.

Rajah put up one paw and batted at a falling copper leaf. Old Sillerton lifted his Egyptian head and sneezed. There were witch fires in the blue-hazed streets again, and on the air the smell of burning witch tobacco.

Kristin and Suzanne tripped by in their ghost suits singing, to the tune of *The Irish Washerwoman*, some doggerel they had picked up from Professor Desmond:

> *McGinnis is dead*
> *And McCarthy don't know it.*
> *McCarthy is dead*
> *And McGinnis don't know it.*
> *They're both of them dead in the very same bed,*
> *And neither one knows that the other is dead.*

Only to make a good song even better, the little ghosts stretched out *McGinnis* to *McGoonis*.

Professor Desmond found himself beating time with the self-conscious pride of a creator in a double sense: as author of the doggerel in question, and as collaborator in the joint production of *prima donna* Kristin. And, as he thumped his rake in jigging tempo, he coined an epigram. The Irish, bless them, he said to himself, are a great race, and a vanishing one. The friendly sons of St. Patrick are not friendly enough with the apparently friendlier daughters of that same Hibernian saint. Perhaps their ancestral musical idiom was to blame. It takes two to tango, but only one to jig. He must remember to spring that one on Mother.

At 9:30 in the evening Mrs. Desmond set down her yarn and knitting needles and looked across the table at Sheila.

"Finished with your homework, Sheila?" she asked.

"Not yet," said Sheila. "We have to write some sentences about those people in the book."

Professor Desmond, who hated verbal imprecision, slammed down his magazine.

"What people in what book?" he demanded.

"Oh, you know," said Sheila cheerfully.

"I most distinctly do not know," said Professor Desmond. "How should I know?"

"Oh," said Sheila, "Mother Cabrini and Hendrik Hudson, and people like that."

"Well," said Professor Desmond. "You just get cracking on Mother Cabrini and Hendrik Hudson and people like that. It's late."

"How many zones are there?" asked Moira. "Seven?"

"Your turn, Toby," said Professor Desmond. "Don't forget to count in the Intemperate zone we live in."

"Now don't confuse the child, John," said Mrs. Desmond mildly. "You know you love it around here."

At ten p.m., with all the children in bed but Karen, who had gone to the Friday movies courtesy of the neighborhood car pool, Professor Desmond dialed Toronto — there was no American television or radio coverage of the title fight — and leaned back against his three-way pillow to enjoy the bout. This was the big one. Only the heavyweights counted in the long run. With Ruby Goldstein as referee, the fighters ought to keep moving nicely.

Just as the bell sounded for the third round, the front door bell pinged, too. Professor Desmond sighed a little in relief. They were all home now, Karen, too. They were all under the same roof again.

The child moved in her womb, waking Mrs. Desmond. For a few minutes she could not get to sleep again. Then, as the colonial clock chimed twelve, she dropped off once more into a dreamless slumber.

Downstairs, in the deep quiet after midnight, the Oseberg ship cast a sharp shadow on the moonlit mantel wall. The moonlight seemed colder in quality than last night's. A light frost glimmered on the slates. In the rose beds the delicate folded petals were beginning to turn a little black. But only the great Arctic white owl, flying noiseless on its huge northern pinions, actually saw the first white rubrics of winter. When, two nights before, it had flown across Georgian Bay, there were already a few spiraling flakes over Christian Island. Tonight, with the moon cold on Lake Erie, the great bird sat on the Council Rock, gold eyes glowing in the velvet shadow, and stared at the little moon-blanched beach house that was once more shuttered up till spring. Nothing else stirred in the Canadian night.